page 37

 700g  80g 3g

 400g 50g 2g

page 46

$\frac{4}{5}$ 6 3

$\frac{5}{7}$ $\frac{3}{4}$ $\frac{6}{8}$

page 48

   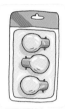 

page 54

page 53

page 58

$\frac{4}{5}$ $\frac{5}{6}$

$\frac{2}{3}$ $\frac{3}{4}$

page 61

£2.25	89p
85p	£1.30
75p	£1.50

page 63

Extra stickers

 Well done! Well done! Well done!

 Well done!   Well done! Well done!

page 3

page 8

page 9

page 13

page 14

page 16

page 22

page 23

page 24

page 31

page 69

page 73

time	time	time	place
place	person	person	event

page 76

sion	sion	tion	tion
sion	sion	tion	tion

sion	tion

page 78

page 84

eyes	dog	many	diary
children	phone	a	two
his	people	that	the

page 98

Alice   Jenny

Mike   Steve

page 103

| 6 | 2 | 8 | 8 |
| 1 | 4 | 2 | 5 |

page 111

| 8 | 6 | 5 |
| 8 | 0 | 1 |

page 115

<	<
>	>
=	<
0.25	0.2
0.07	0.02
0.5	0.05

page 121

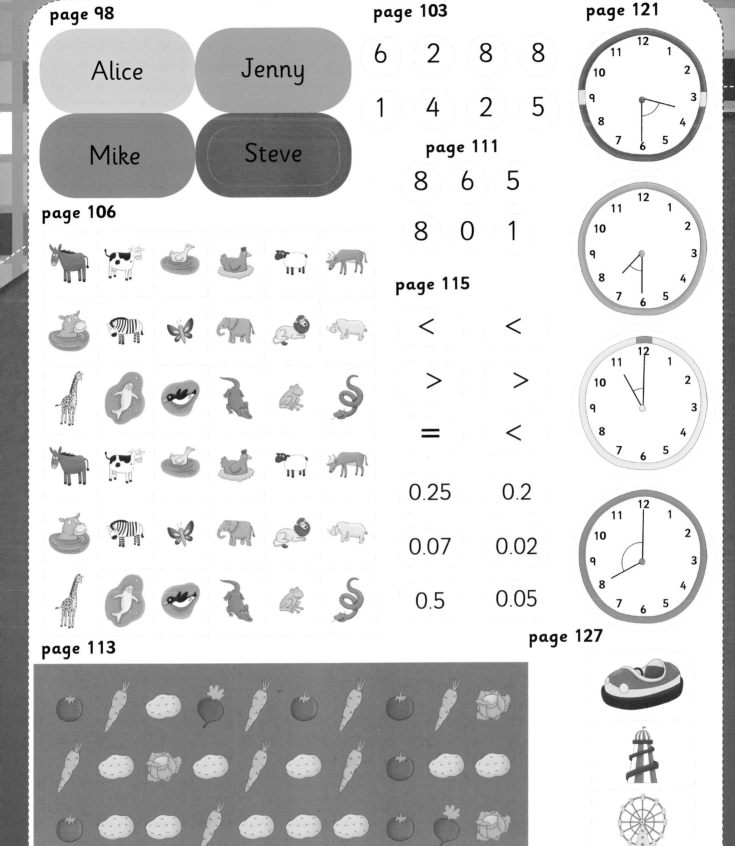

page 106

page 113

page 114

page 127

7-8 years

Leap Ahead
BUMPER
Workbook

Key Stage 2

ENGLISH

Home learning made **FUN!**

igloobooks

Writing About the Past

For each sentence below, choose the correct past progressive tense ('was' or 'were') by circling it, then fill in the blank with the correct verb from the list in the circle below.

I was / were .... my orange juice.

We was / were .... colourful party hats.

He was / were .... dinner with his friend.

We ran to the park so we was / were ....

Her dog was / were .... in the mud!

They was / were .... to the music.

She was / were .... because it was dark outside.

wearing
drinking
eating
scared
rolling
listening
tired

Answers on page 32

Past Progressives

Read the sentences below and add the correct past progressive tense. The first one has been done for you.

I ....was........ running along the path when I saw a dog dart in front of me! It .... black with white spots on its tail. I didn't want to scare it, so I stopped running. I .... just about to call after the dog when I saw my friend. He ran over and said he had seen it too. We .... going to see if it was wearing a collar but it had disappeared!

Tim and Tom had pizza for their dinner last night. Stick the pizza sticker in the box below then finish the description of the pizza, using the picture to help you.

Last night, Tim and Tom shared a delicious homemade pizza. It was topped with their mum's special tomato sauce.

....

....

....

....

....

....

Answers on page 32

PARENT TIP: Remind your child that 'was' is used when we talk about a single person and 'were' is used when we talk about a pair or groups. E.g. He was dancing / They were dancing.

Playing Pirates

Here are some sentences written by one of the children in the picture, who were playing pirates. Choose from the list of past tense words to fill in the blanks.

Last night, we played pirates! After all the lights were out, we put on our eye patches and pirate hats, which we had .... under the bed.

We turned the toy chest into a treasure chest and .... that our bed was a huge pirate ship.

was
pretended
sailed
hidden
opened
jumped
were

We .... the seas, using a rolled up magazine as our telescope to spy on other ships sailing by. We even saw a pirate with one leg! He .... scary.

We .... just about to reach an island when my mum .... the bedroom door! We quickly .... under the covers and pretended to be asleep!

4

Answers on page 32

A Trip to the Woods

Read about the class visit to the woods, then answer the questions.

a

Class 3 Trip to Upton Woods:
Tuesday 17th February

The children examined leaves,
conkers and acorns, and they
enjoyed playing in the leaves.
It was very muddy and one
child even got mud in her boots.
One boy did appear to be lost for
a short time, which was worrying,
but then we discovered he was
playing hide-and-seek with Dylan.
All in all, it was a pleasant trip.

b

Sarah's report:

We went to Upton Woods
in a minibus. It was a very
cold day. I collected conkers
and acorns and Mrs Williams
saw a fox. There was lots
of mud and some of it
went in my boots!

Dylan's report:

c

We went to the woods with
Mrs Williams. It was really
muddy and there were lots of
leaves. I jumped in them, then
I played hide-and-seek with
Josh. It was exciting!

1. **Which report was written by the teacher, Mrs Williams?**

   ....

2. **Who talks about a fox in their report?**

   ....

3. **Who seemed to get lost in the woods? Why?**

   ....

   ....

4. **What was Mrs Williams worried about?**

   ....

5. **How did Dylan feel about the trip?**

   ....

Answers on page 32

Cartoon Stories

Look at each of the cartoons below. Write in the speech bubbles what you think each person is saying, then write a short sentence below each cartoon to describe the action. Some have been done for you.

1

Is this the bank? Give me all your money!

I'm afraid you've got it wrong, sir. This is a bottle bank.

The robber ran up to the counter. The man looked puzzled.

2

3

The Full Story

Use the pictures and speech bubbles on the opposite page to make three short stories of your own. The words in the speech bubbles should be shown in speech marks.

Story 1

A robber went into a bank. He said, "Is this the bank? Give me all your money!" The man behind the counter looked puzzled. "I'm afraid you've got it wrong, sir," he said. "This is a bottle bank."

Story 2

....

....

....

....

....

....

....

Story 3

....

....

....

....

....

....

Present Perfect Tense

What have you done this week? Write three sentences using the sentence starter 'I have'. An example has been written for you.

I have watched a film at the cinema.

I have ....

I have ....

I have ....

Use your sentences to write a short diary entry using the structure below. Place the diary sticker from the sticker sheet into the box.

Dear Diary,

I have been very busy.

I have .... ,

which was ....

I have also ....

....

Answers on page 32

PARENT TIP: The present perfect tense uses the verb 'to have' plus the past tense version of the second verb. E.g. He has landed. / They have jumped. / I have spent my money.

Fact or Fiction?

Read the texts below. In the square box, write 'N' for non-fiction or 'F' for fiction. Then decide whether the text is 1st person or 3rd person and write the answer in the rectangular box. Finally, find the matching sticker and stick it in the big box. The first one has been done for you.

1st person	my	I	mine	me	our
3rd person	he	she	they	it	their

1. Today a school was closed when water flooded the classrooms. Pupils had to go home. One child said, "It's not fair. It was my turn at the art table."

N

3rd person

2. Yesterday I went to hospital to have my appendix out. I thought I would be scared, but I was okay.

3. Once upon a time, a little girl lived by the edge of a big wood.

4. Horatio: I think it's time you went to bed, Gertrude. Gertrude: Yes, my head is spinning.

Answers on page 32

9

Punctuate It

Use question marks, exclamation marks and full stops to complete these sentences.

!	.	?

(1) What's your name ☐ My name is George ☐

(2) What a day it has been ☐ I think I need to go home ☐

(3) This is the best cake ever ☐ What do you think of it ☐

(4) No ☐ Don't go in there ☐

(5) I haven't got any money ☐ Have you ☐

Look at this picture.

Write a question, a statement and an exclamation about it.

Remember to use an exclamation mark, full stop and question mark in the correct places.

....

....

....

....

....

Answers on page 32

Adverbs

Some adverbs are used to explain time. Choose the correct adverbs from the box to complete the story. One has been done for you.

After a few seconds	After a few minutes	Later that day	Next	A while later	Then	~~Last week~~

~~Last week~~ I went to watch a motorbike race at a local racing track. We arrived and took our seats on the stand and there was suddenly a very loud roar! .... , the motorbikes whizzed past. The crowd cheered.

.... , we heard a tremendous crash. One of the bikes had hit another bike. .... , an emergency ambulance arrived, but the rider of the motorbike was fine.

.... , the race ended and we sat by the track to eat a delicious picnic.

.... , I met one of the motorbike racers who was standing near the track. It was exciting to meet him and I got a great photo with him. .... , we had to head back home. What a great day it was!

Answers on page 32

Parts of Speech

Read the story above again. Can you complete the lists of words below?

The first word for each list has been done for you.

5 adjectives (describing words): delicious, ...

5 nouns (objects or things): race, ...

5 verbs (doing/action words): went, ...

11

Prepositional Phrases

The sentences below use prepositional phrases. Read each sentence then circle the preposition and underline the prepositional phrase. One has been done for you.

The pirate is (in) the cave.

The treasure map is under the palm tree.

The treasure is in the chest.

The coconuts are on the tree.

The dolphins are in the sea.

The treasure chest is beside the shipwreck.

The seagull sat on the sand.

Answers on page 32

Write three sentences about the treasure chest picture below. Remember to use prepositional phrases.

....

....

....

....

....

....

....

Pirate Island

In the picture below, draw a circle around the castle, knight, shipwreck and the trees. Then write a sentence about each object and include a prepositional phrase. One has been done for you.

The lady is in the cave.

Once you've completed all the sentences, place the well done sticker from the sticker sheet in this box.

Expanding Noun Phrases

Write some descriptions of this island. Expand before the noun using an adjective, and expand after the noun using a prepositional phrase. Then place the fish stickers from the sticker sheet into the sticker box below, and write about the fish. Two descriptions have been written for you.

little gnomes
by the
cliff edge

14

wooden
shipwreck
next to
the hill

Extending Sentences

Stick one pirate sticker in each box below. Write a simple sentence about each pirate then extend it using a co-ordinating conjunction (e.g. and/but/or). Two sentences have been completed for you.

Simple sentence: The pirate had a beard.

Extended sentence: The pirate had a beard and a noisy parrot.

Simple sentence: The pirate looked at his map.

Extended sentence: The pirate looked at his map but he still couldn't find the treasure.

Simple sentence: ....

....

Extended sentence: ....

....

Simple sentence: ....

....

Extended sentence: ....

....

Simple sentence: ....

....

Extended sentence: ....

....

Subordinating Conjunctions

Here is a sentence with a subordinating conjunction.
The parts of the sentence are labelled for you.

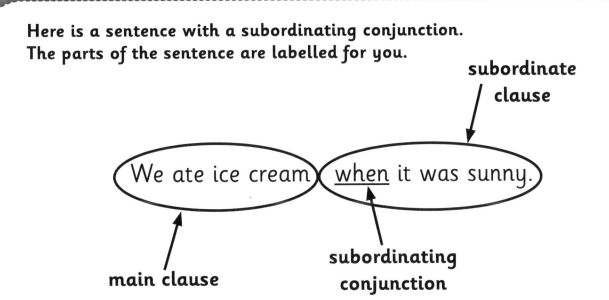

subordinate
clause

We ate ice cream — when it was sunny.

main clause

subordinating
conjunction

Write your own complex sentences. Choose a subordinating conjunction
from the box below then finish the sentence with a subordinate clause.
The main clause has already been written for you.

because	when	after	before	while

We went for a walk ....

....

She looked at the cat ....

....

They ran to the park ....

....

Tom and Susan did some painting ....

....

She jumped into the muddy puddle ....

....

....

Silly Sports

Oh, dear! Sports day is in a real muddle and all of the races are going wrong. Write a poster to tell the children the rules for each race. Add a title to the poster and remember to use numbers or bullet points to organise your instructions. The first set of rules has been done for you.

PARENT TIP: Explain that, when you write instructions, you must remember to be clear. Instruction sentences often start with a verb, for example, 'stand', 'take', 'put'. Adverbs, such as 'next', 'then' and 'finally' can also be used.

Egg and Spoon Race

1. Stand in a line at the start.

2. Take one egg and one spoon and put the egg on the spoon.

4. When the whistle blows, walk or run to the end without dropping the egg from the spoon.

5. The first person to finish without dropping their egg is the winner.

Searching for Suffixes

Can you match the descriptions below to the correct meanings? All of the answers contain one of the suffixes 'ment', 'ful' or 'less'.

Description

a. When you disagree with someone.

b. Taking a lot of care.

c. Like a baby, someone who can't do anything for him or herself.

d. Without any purpose.

e. The paving next to a road that you walk on.

f. Very nice to look at or listen to.

Meaning

1. pavement

2. argument

3. beautiful

4. pointless

5. careful

6. helpless

The words below are missing suffixes. Can you add the correct suffix from the box below to complete each word?

ly	sure	ture	tion	sion	ous

posi......   sad.......   friend.......

careful......   pos.......   tor.......

trea......   jeal.......   danger.......

pollu......   solu......   ero.......

Answers on page 32

Alphabet Fun

Answer the questions below. Use a dictionary to help you.

1. Which letter is halfway in the alphabet? ....

2. How far through the alphabet is the letter h? ....

3. Will you find the word 'monkey' at the beginning, middle or end of the dictionary? ....

4. Will you find the word 'zebra' at the beginning, middle or end of the dictionary? ....

5. Will you find the word 'cheetah' at the beginning, middle or end of the dictionary?

....

6. Will you find the word 'trophy' near the beginning, middle or end of the dictionary?

....

The list of words below has been scrambled! Rewrite the words beginning with 'b' in alphabetical order to 2 places. Rewrite the words beginning with 'g' in alphabetical order to 3 places. Some have been done for you.

bridge	ball	girl	
boy		grumpy	
bench		grin	
buzz		grow	
ball		green	
boost		grab	
big	bridge	gap	
bib		go	

Answers on page 32

21

It's Mine!

Look at the words on each of the signs and add apostrophes in the correct places. Find stickers to give everyone back their lost possessions.

a Ladys hat

b Sallys doll

c Dans bike

d Friends dog

Astronauts boot

e

f Owners slipper

Answers on page 32

PARENT TIP: Explain that apostrophes that come after a noun or name and are followed by **s** mean that somebody owns something. Apostrophes can also be used to show that some letters have been missed out.

Contractions Practice

Rewrite the sentences below using an apostrophe somewhere in the words that are in a box. Then match the correct stickers from the sticker sheet with the sentences b, d and f. The first sentence has been written for you.

(a) She has won the trophy!

She's won the trophy!

(b) I do not like this music.

(c) What is the matter with you?

(d) I have not been to this cafe before.

(e) I know they are not at home.

(f) It is never a good idea to argue.

(g) We were not ready in time.

(h) You are not going in!

Answers on page 32

23

Whatever the Weather

Read these three poems about the weather. Find a sticker to show the type of weather described in each poem. Then circle three words in each poem that you like. Think about why you like them.

A darker sky, a colder breeze,
Was that a flash high in the trees?

Time to hurry, time to run.
No sign now of sky or sun.

A rumbling sound and soon a crash.
The sky lights up with a bright, white flash.

Lazing on the warm beach all day,
Hazy palm trees sway from side to side.

Fields so golden and calm,
White clouds in the sky like candy floss.

Cooling down time, a pool-time splash.
No need to rush, no need to dash.

Like a blanket, soft and creeping,
Over fields like water, sleeping.

Through the window there's nothing to see,
Just soft white wisps for company.

Instead of placing a sticker here, draw your own picture based on the poem.

Now write your own poem about the weather.

24

My weather poem:

Try to include a simile and some of the words you circled on the previous page.

....

....

....

....

....

....

....

....

....

....

....

....

....

The Opposite Twins

Meet the opposite twins! Whatever one of them says, the other says the opposite. Can you add 'un', 'dis', 'im', 'il' or 'mis' to each of Twin 1's words to find the opposite? Write them on Twin 2's scarf. The first one has been done for you.

Twin 1

Twin 2

agree

practical

fair

like

understood

legal

trust

loyal

perfect

disagree

Answers on page 32

Big Spelling Test

Can you learn to spell all of these words?

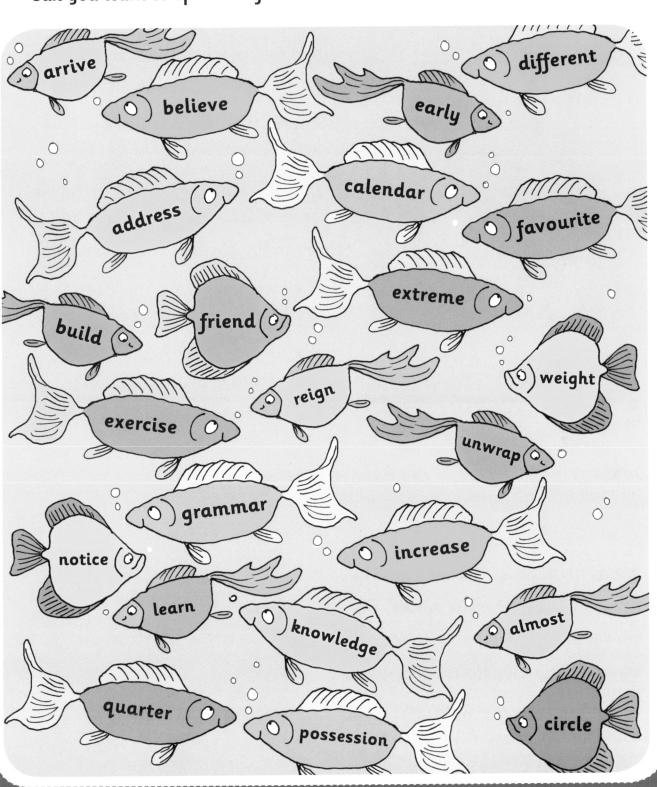

arrive, believe, different, early, calendar, address, favourite, extreme, build, friend, weight, exercise, reign, unwrap, grammar, increase, notice, learn, knowledge, almost, quarter, possession, circle

PARENT TIP: Remember to use the 'read, cover, write, check' method with your child so that they can check their spelling. Other words that children should learn include: actually, bicycle, caught, centre, century, experiment, favourite, February, medicine, material, often, promise.

Proofreading Text

In the text below, correct any spelling mistakes by underlining them and writing the correct version next to the word.

When Ged reached the scene of the crime, he culd see strait away what had happened. Crums, crumbs everywhere. Whoever had taken the cake had been careless. The trail of crumbs lead out of the door and through the garden. They even went over th gate!

Everthing stopped at the curb, though. Ged whistled and his dog, Sniff, arrived in an instant. "Cake." said Ged. "Follow the smell of cake."

In the text below, add in any missing punctuation and correct any punctuation errors.

Sniff ran off along the road so quickly it was hard for Ged to keep up The dog ran down the road, around the corner and stopped outside a bakery. Ged crept quietly around to the back. Peering through a dirty window, he could see three men Between them was an empty plate and some crumbs of chocolate cake? Ged was too late

Evaluating Text

Evaluate and finish the text below by following the instructions.
1. Underline any words in the wrong tense and write the correct words next to them.
2. Find the adjectives in bold, put a line through them, then write a more powerful adjective next to each one.
3. Finish the spooky story on the empty lines.
4. Illustrate the ending in the box below.

He only went into the garden to get his ball, but as he pushes the weeds aside, he noticed that the door to the house was open.

The **big** door creaked as he pushed it. It is too dark to see inside, so he went in further to get a better look. Suddenly, the door swung shut behind him, making him jump. Then, he heard a **little** noise. It was a key turning. At the far end of the **dark** hallway, another door opened slowly. He feels every hair on his head stand up.

....

....

....

....

....

....

....

....

The Story of My Life

Use these pages to write all about yourself and your life. Use adjectives to describe people and places, and use exclamation marks, quotation marks and dates where possible. Plan what you will write using the structure below, then write your final draft on the next page.

Introduction (tell the reader three things about yourself — present tense):

1. ....

2. ....

3. ....

....

Best time in your life (describe people and places — past tense): ....

1. ....

2. ....

3. ....

....

Challenging time in your life (describe people and places — past tense): ....

1. ....

2. ....

3. ....

....

Ending and summary (give one interesting fact and tell the reader ....

about your hopes for the future — future tense): ....

1. ....

2. ....

3. ....

....

....

....

....

....

....

....

....

....

....

....

....

....

....

Use the checklist below to make sure you've included everything. Use the stickers on the sticker sheet to tick off each objective.

- Expanded noun phrases to describe people and places

- Correct punctuation

- Variety of sentence types

- Consistent tense

- Correct spelling

Answers

Page 2: Writing About the Past
I <u>was drinking</u> my orange juice. / We <u>were wearing</u> colourful party hats. / He <u>was eating</u> dinner with his friend. / We ran to the park so we <u>were tired</u>. / Her dog <u>was rolling</u> in the mud. / They <u>were listening</u> to the music. / She <u>was scared</u> because it was dark outside.

Page 3: Past Progressives
I <u>was</u> running ... It <u>was</u> black with .... I <u>was</u> just about to ... We <u>were</u> going ...

Page 4: Playing Pirates
... we had <u>hidden</u> under the bed ... a treasure chest and <u>pretended</u> that our bed ... We <u>sailed</u> the seas ... He <u>was</u> scary. We <u>were</u> just about to ... my mum <u>opened</u> the bedroom door! We quickly <u>jumped</u> under the covers ...

Page 5: A Trip to the Woods
1 — Report (a) was written by Mrs Williams.
2 — Sarah's report (b) talks about a fox.
3 — Josh seemed to get lost in the woods because he was playing hide-and-seek.
4 — She was worried that one boy went missing.
5 — Dylan felt excited.

Page 8: Present Perfect Tense
Answers could include: I have played in the garden. I have baked a cake. I have been to the seaside.

Page 9: Fact or Fiction?
1 — N/3rd person (newspaper).
2 — N/1st person (diary).
3 — F/3rd person (story book).
4 — F/1st person (play script).

Page 10: Punctuate It
Answers may vary.
1. What's your name? My name is George.
2. What a day it has been! I think I need to go home.
3. This is the best cake ever! What do you think of it?
4. No! Don't go in there.
5. I haven't got any money. Have you?

Page 11: Adverbs
Answers may vary. Here is one example:
<u>Last week</u> I went ... suddenly a very loud roar! <u>After a few seconds</u>, the motorbikes ... crowd cheered. <u>After a few minutes</u>, we heard a ... another bike. <u>Next</u>, an emergency ... was fine. <u>A while later</u>, the ... <u>Later that day</u>, I met ... great photo with him. <u>Then</u>, we had to head back home ...

Page 12: Prepositional Phrases
The pirate is (in) the cave.
The treasure map is (under) the palm tree.
The treasure is (in) the chest.
The coconuts are (on) the tree.
The dolphins are (in) the sea.
The treasure chest is (beside) the shipwreck.
The seagull sat (on) the sand.

Page 20: Searching for Suffixes
a – 2, b – 5, c – 6, d – 4, e – 1, f – 3
posi<u>tion</u>, careful<u>ly</u>, trea<u>sure</u>, pollu<u>tion</u>, sad<u>ly</u>, pos<u>ture</u>, jeal<u>ous</u>, solu<u>tion</u>, friend<u>ly</u>, tor<u>ture</u>, danger<u>ous</u>, ero<u>sion</u>

Page 21: Alphabet Fun
1: M, 2: 8th, 3: middle, 4: end, 5: beginning, 6: near the end
ball, bench, bib, big, boost, boy, bridge, buzz
gap, girl, go, grab, green, grin, grow, grumpy

Page 22: It's Mine!
a: Lady's hat b: Sally's doll c: Dan's bike
d: Friend's dog e: Astronaut's boot f: Owner's slipper

Page 23: Contractions Practice
a: She's b: don't c: What's d: haven't e: they're
f: It's g: weren't h: You're

Page 26: The Opposite Twins
agree - disagree
practical - impractical
fair - unfair
like - dislike
understood - misunderstood
legal - illegal
trust - distrust
loyal - disloyal
perfect - imperfect

Page 28: Proofreading Text
When Ged reached the scene of the crime, he c<u>o</u>uld see strai<u>ght</u> away what had happened. Crum<u>b</u>s, crumbs everywhere. Whoever had taken the cake had been careless. The trail of crumbs lead out of the door and through the garden. They even went over th<u>e</u> gate! Ever<u>y</u>thing stopped at the curb, though. Ged whistled and his dog, Sniff, arrived in an instant. "Cake." said Ged. "Follow the smell of cake."

Sniff ran off along the road so quickly it was hard for Ged to keep up<u>.</u> The dog ran down the road, around the corner and stopped outside a bakery. Ged crept quietly around to the back. Peering through a dirty window, he could see three men<u>.</u> Between them was an empty plate and some crumbs of chocolate cake<u>!</u> Ged was too late<u>.</u>

Leap Ahead
BUMPER
Workbook

MATHS

Home learning made FUN!

Numbers to 1000

Sam is an air-traffic controller. He must land the planes in the correct order. Match the information from the control tower with the numbers on the planes.

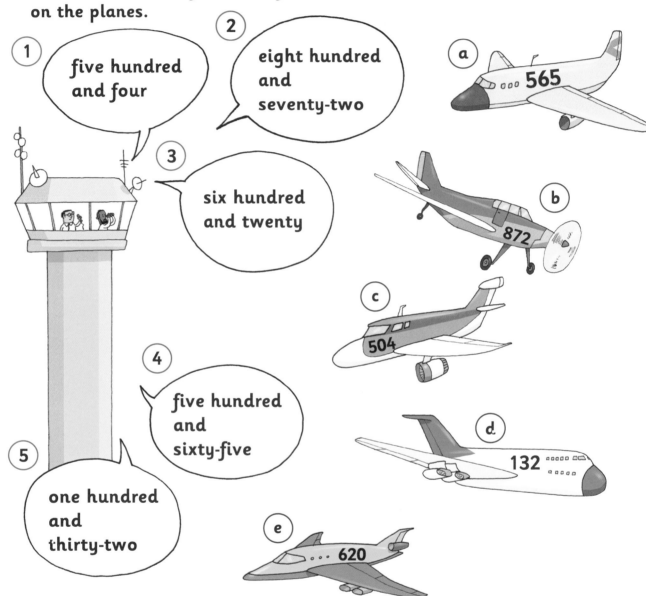

1. five hundred and four
2. eight hundred and seventy-two
3. six hundred and twenty
4. five hundred and sixty-five
5. one hundred and thirty-two

a. 565
b. 872
c. 504
d. 132
e. 620

Write these flight numbers in words.

Flight 358 = _____

Flight 721 = _____

Flight 402 = _____

Flight 630 = _____

Answers on page 64

10 and 100

The flights last for different amounts of time. Flights to countries that are further away take longer. Flights usually run on time, but sometimes they arrive early or are a little delayed.

Complete this chart showing delays and early arrivals.

Flight number	Planned flight duration (mins)	Event	New flight duration (mins)
BA 248	480	+10 mins	490 mins
EJ 529	725	−100 mins	
AA 372	631	+100 mins	
SB 843	894	−10 mins	
KG 654	79	+10 mins	
BP 459	128	+100 mins	
GP 674	245	−10 mins	
FR 328	473	−100 mins	

Fill in the chart below with the correct flight times:

−100 from START time	−10 from START time	START	+10 from START time	+100 from START time
		648		

Answers on page 64

PARENT TIP: With your child, practise saying numbers that are 1, 10 and 100 more or less than a given 3-digit number. Mark a dice with +1, −1, +10, −10, +100, −100. Start on 500 and take turns to roll the dice and complete the calculation. The player with the largest number after an agreed number of rolls is the winner.

Order Numbers to 1000

Jack and Sammie work at the post office. They need to put these letters in order for delivery. Write each house number in the correct sequence in the boxes below. The first one has been done for you.

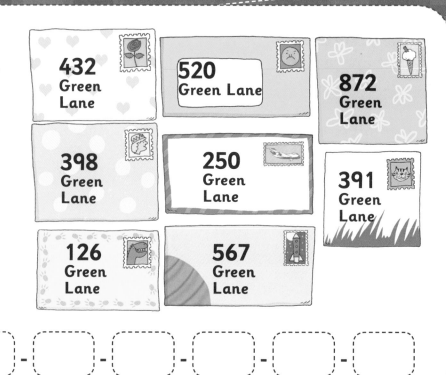

126 - ◯ - ◯ - ◯ - ◯ - ◯ - ◯ - ◯

The parcel vans have a delivery map. Join each parcel to the correct position on the number line below.

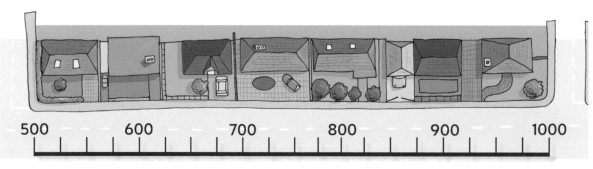

500   600   700   800   900   1000

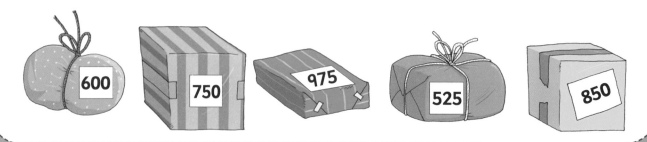

600   750   975   525   850

Circle the largest number in each pair.

a	b	c	d	e	f
383 349	635 653	492 421	556 565	279 229	736 739

Answers on page 64

Place Value to 1000

These parcels must be weighed to calculate postage. The weights come in multiples of 100, 10 and 1. Choose the correct weight stickers to match these parcels.

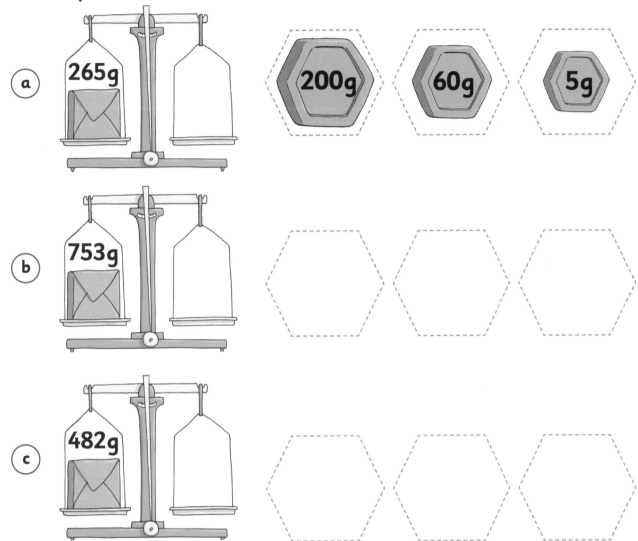

Complete these place value additions:

$479 = 400 +$ ⬚ $+ 9$ $372 =$ ⬚ $+ 70 +$ ⬚

$600 + 20 + 3 =$ ⬚ $500 +$ ⬚ $+ 6 = 546$

Answers on page 64

PARENT TIP: Practise partitioning and recombining numbers with your child. This is an essential skill that your child will use later when adding and subtracting. Write multiples of 100, 10 and 1 on pieces of card and place them in sets, face down on the table. Take turns to choose one card from each set and recombine to make a 3-digit number.

37

Adding Numbers

These deep-sea divers are getting ready to go in the water.

Join their wetsuit numbers to the correct air cylinder.

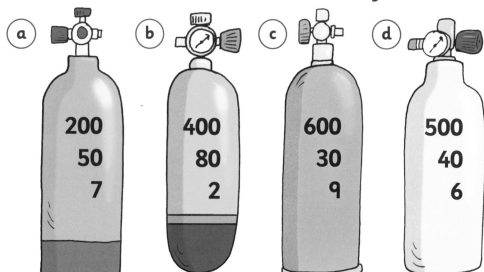

The air cylinder numbers need changing for the next set of divers. Complete the calculations below to find out the new numbers.

482 + 4 = [ ]

546 + 30 = [ ]

639 + 200 = [ ]

257 + 40 = [ ]

Answers on page 64

PARENT TIP: Play a number game with your child. Choose a start number then roll a dice to see how many hundreds to add to your number (e.g. roll 3, add 300). Roll again to see how many tens to add and then roll to see how many ones to add. What number did you end up on? The winner is the person who has made the largest number.

The team of deep-sea divers has been counting different types of fish they have seen this year.

bass	cod	eel	ray	turbot	sole
352	521	476	215	622	133

Calculate the combinations below for their records. Use the boxes below for your working out.

bass + cod (352) + (521) = (873)

turbot + ray ( ) + ( ) = ( )

cod + sole ( ) + ( ) = ( )

eel + ray ( ) + ( ) = ( )

1. Which fish did they see the most? _____

2. Which fish did they see the least? _____

3. How many more turbot did they see than cod? _____

Answers on page 64

Perimeters

Farmer Ted's sheep keep escaping! He needs to build new fencing around all of his fields. First he must calculate how much fencing is needed.

Field 1

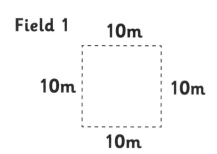

He starts at one corner and walks around each side of the field to get a measurement for each side. He adds the measurements together. This gives him the perimeter.
10m + 10m + 10m + 10m = 40m fencing.

Work out the fencing needed for the other fields. Write the measurements in the boxes below.

$$\bigcirc + \bigcirc + \bigcirc + \bigcirc = \bigcirc$$

Field 2

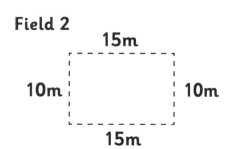

Field 3

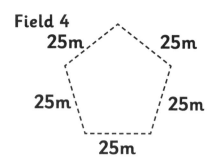

$$\bigcirc + \bigcirc + \bigcirc = \bigcirc$$

Field 4

25m 25m
25m 25m
25m

Working out space:

Field 5

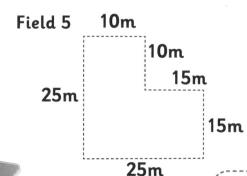

Working out space:

40

Answers on page 64

Farmer Ted already has 100m of spare fencing.

Which two fields could he fix now? ....

How much more fencing does he need to order? ....

Draw two different fields below that each have a perimeter of 16cm.

Answers on page 64

PARENT TIP: Talk to your child about the perimeter being the distance around the edge of a shape. Find perimeters of objects around the house, such as picture frames, books and table mats. Try to include some shapes that are not four sided. Explain that shapes that appear bigger may not necessarily have the longest perimeter.

Pictograms

The recycling men have been sorting out the boxes they have collected from Fishpool Street.

Calculate the total number of boxes of each type.

Key:  = 5 boxes

		Total
Paper	🗑️🗑️🗑️🗑️🗑️🗑️	
Glass	🗑️🗑️🗑️	
Plastic	🗑️🗑️🗑️🗑️🗑️🗑️🗑️🗑️	
Cardboard	🗑️🗑️🗑️🗑️	
Cans	🗑️🗑️	

Which item had the most collected? _____

How many boxes of glass were collected? _____

How much more paper was collected than cans? _____

Of which item were 20 boxes collected? _____

One van came back late and brought 5 boxes of glass and 10 boxes of cardboard. Add this information to the pictogram.

Answers on page 64

42

Time Durations

Some roads have more houses and it takes longer for the recycling men to collect the boxes. Here are the start and finish times for each road. Work out how long it took to collect the boxes from each road.

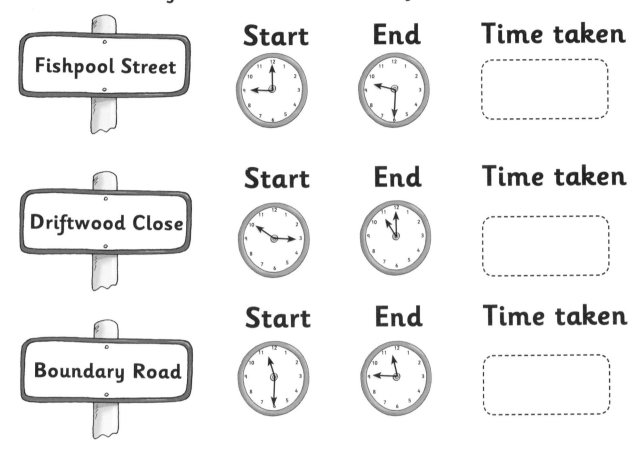

Fishpool Street

Start   End   Time taken

Driftwood Close

Start   End   Time taken

Boundary Road

Start   End   Time taken

Mersey Way is the final road for them to collect from. They start at 12:00 and they finish 20 minutes later. Show their final finish time on the clock face below.

Mersey Way

Which road took the longest to collect from?

_____

Calculate how long it took the team to collect from all four roads. They began at 9:00 in Fishpool Street and finished when Mersey Way had been collected.

Total time taken = _____

Answers on page 64

Subtracting Numbers

Jacob works for a building firm. He is in charge of stock and must make sure they don't run out of equipment.

Equipment in stock on Monday:

bricks	tiles	pipes	switches	paint
957	876	387 metres	168	456 litres

On Friday, Jacob must change the stock list because some equipment has been used during the week. Calculate the remaining stock. Use the subtraction methods you have been taught in school.

bricks	tiles	pipes
957 in stock	876 in stock	387 metres in stock
300 used	50 used	3 metres used
Working out space	Working out space	Working out space

switches	paint
168 in stock	456 litres in stock
29 used	163 litres used
Working out space	Working out space

Answers on page 64

Lots of workers have been using nails. Jacob must subtract the amount each worker has used to calculate the number of nails left.

650 nails

MONDAY

John has used 50 nails

650 – 50 = ⬚

⬚ nails left

TUESDAY

Mick has used 100 nails

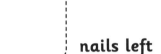

⬚ – 100 = ⬚

⬚ nails left

WEDNESDAY

Sam has used 6 nails

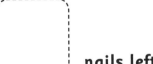

⬚ – 6 = ⬚

⬚ nails left

THURSDAY

Amanda has used 80 nails

⬚ – 80 = ⬚

⬚ nails left

FRIDAY

Bob has used 200 nails

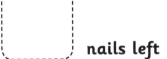

⬚ – 200 = ⬚

⬚ nails left

Nails left at the end of the week = ⬚

Answer on page 64

PARENT TIP: Play a game with your child. Have a target board drawn on paper with numbered sections, e.g. 1, 5, 20, 45, 60. Roll a coin and see which number it lands on. Start on 200 and keep subtracting the numbers landed on. The first player to 0 wins. Change the start number or the numbers on the target board to increase the difficulty.

Fractions

Follow the instructions to help Sarah shade fractions of these shapes.

Colour in
$\frac{1}{6}$

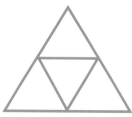

Colour in
$\frac{1}{4}$

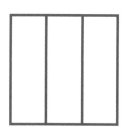

Colour in
$\frac{1}{3}$

Colour in
$\frac{2}{5}$

Colour in
$\frac{3}{8}$

Answers on page 64

Find the stickers with the correct answers to complete these additions.

a) $\frac{1}{4} + \frac{2}{4} = $ ⬚

b) $\frac{2}{5} + \frac{2}{5} = $ ⬚

c) $\frac{1}{3} + \frac{1}{3} = $ ⬚

d) $\frac{3}{7} + \frac{2}{7} = $ ⬚

e) $\frac{4}{6} + \frac{1}{6} = $ ⬚

f) $\frac{4}{8} + \frac{2}{8} = $ ⬚

46

Answers on page 64

These pirates are sharing the treasure. Circle the fraction of gold coins each pirate wants.

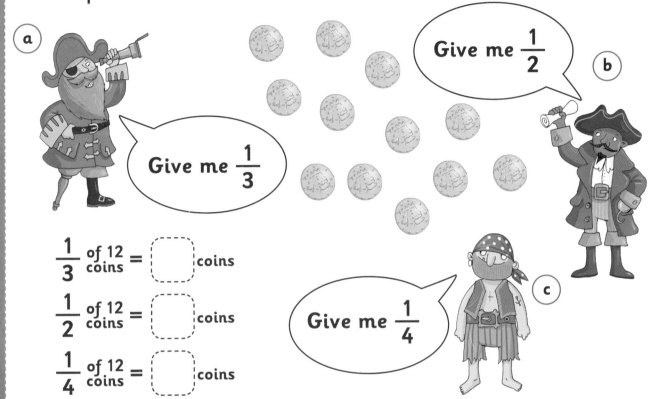

a

Give me $\frac{1}{3}$

Give me $\frac{1}{2}$ b

Give me $\frac{1}{4}$ c

$\frac{1}{3}$ of 12 coins = ⬚ coins

$\frac{1}{2}$ of 12 coins = ⬚ coins

$\frac{1}{4}$ of 12 coins = ⬚ coins

Are there enough coins to give each pirate the number he wants? Circle the correct answer.

YES / NO

Answers on page 64

Colour $\frac{1}{2}$ of each pirate flag. Make each flag look different.

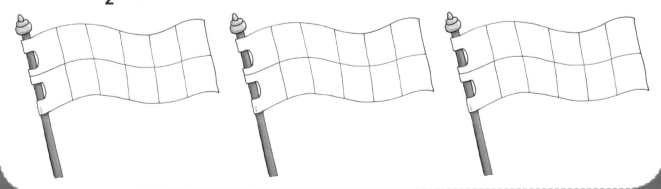

PARENT TIP: Practise finding simple fractions of quantities at home. For example, if you give Amy ½ of the sweets, how many does she have? Share the grapes, ¼ each. How many do you have each? Read ¾ of the book now. How many pages is that?

47

Multiply by 3, 4 and 8

Stuart the mechanic has a delivery of new parts. The indicator bulbs are in packs of 3. Put the bulb stickers in the spaces below. Count in 3s to see how many have arrived.

| 3 | 6 | ⬚ | ⬚ | ⬚ | ⬚ |

= ⬚ bulbs in total

Complete these orders:

Customer 1:
2 packs of 3 bulbs = ⬚ bulbs

Customer 2:
3 packs of 3 bulbs = ⬚ bulbs

Customer 3:
6 packs of 3 bulbs = ⬚ bulbs

Customer 4:
5 packs of 3 bulbs = ⬚ bulbs

The nuts and bolts have been split into 2 groups.
How many are in each group?

⬚ bolts

⬚ nuts

Answers on page 64

In the tyre workshop, each car needs 4 new tyres.
Calculate the number of tyres needed each day.

	Monday	Tuesday	Wednesday	Thursday	Friday
Numbers of cars	6	3	8	4	5
Tyres needed	6 x 4 = 24				

Some cars have arrived for a service. They need to have new spark plugs.

These 7 cars need 4 spark plugs each.

How many spark plugs are needed in total?

These 6 cars need 8 spark plugs each.

How many spark plugs are needed in total?

Complete this number sequence and solve the multiplications.

8 ⬚ ⬚ 32 ⬚ ⬚ 56 ⬚ ⬚ 80

3 x 8 = ⬚   6 x 8 = ⬚   4 x 8 = ⬚

5 x 8 = ⬚   7 x 8 = ⬚   9 x 8 = ⬚

Answers on page 64

PARENT TIP: Your child needs to understand how multiplication tables are built up by repeatedly adding the same number a certain number of times, e.g. 3 x 4 = 4 + 4 + 4. Counting on in steps of this number will help. However, they also need to know individual facts from the 3, 4 and 8 multiplication tables from memory.

49

Measures

Amy and Calum work on the Space Station measuring things they find in outer space.

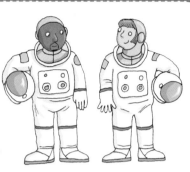

Amy measured the width of these craters in centimetres, but Calum measured them in metres. Join Calum's measurements to the correct craters. Circle the widest crater.

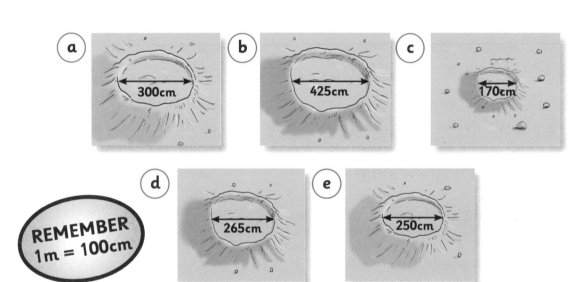

a 300cm

b 425cm

c 170cm

d 265cm

e 250cm

REMEMBER
1m = 100cm

1.7m   3m   4.25m   2.5m   2.65m

Amy weighed these rocks. Write their weights.

REMEMBER
1kg = 1000g

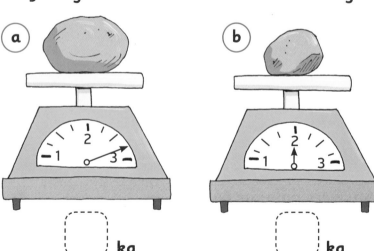

a [   ] kg

b [   ] kg

c [   ] kg

Circle the heaviest rock.

Answers on page 64

Calum has measured the length of some icicles. He needs to add some of the lengths together. Can you help him?

(a) 20cm + 41cm = [ ]

(b) 35cm + 22cm = [ ]

(c) 150cm + 34cm = [ ]

(d) 245cm + 20cm = [ ]

(e) 325cm + 75cm = [ ]

(f) 62cm + 27cm = [ ]

The last job for Amy was to melt some of the icicles and measure the amount of liquid that resulted. Write the measurements.

Jug 1

Jug 2

Jug 3

[ ] ml   [ ] ml   [ ] ml

Calculate the capacity difference between:

Jug 3 and Jug 1   [ ] ml – [ ] ml = [ ]

Jug 1 and Jug 2   [ ] ml – [ ] ml = [ ]

Answers on page 64

PARENT TIP: Your child needs to understand and use the relationship between centimetres and metres. Write some measurements on card, including equivalent pairs, e.g. 250cm and 2.5m. Put them face down, then take turns to select two cards. If they are a pair, keep them. If not, return them to the table. The player to find the most pairs is the winner.

Multiplication

These cattle ranchers are moving their cattle. Use the grid method to calculate the cattle in each group. The first one has been done for you.

3 fields with 26 cattle in each

(a)

x	20	6
3	60 + 18 = 78	

2 fields with 34 cattle in each

(b)

x	30	4
2	◯ + ◯ = ◯	

4 fields with 17 cattle in each

(c)

x	10	7
4	◯ + ◯ = ◯	

5 fields with 24 cattle in each

(d)

x	20	4
5	◯ + ◯ = ◯	

They need to carry enough water for the trip. For one day, they need 26 litres. Work out how much they need for a 2-day trip, a 4-day trip and an 8-day trip. You can use doubling to help you.

2-day trip

4-day trip

8-day trip

Answers on page 64

Analogue and Digital

The cattle ranchers split themselves into small groups and arrange to meet at various times during the trip.

Some wear digital watches but others have clock faces (analogue). Join the equivalent times.

a 5:45
b
c 3:30
d
e 4:00
f
g 8:15
h 10:20
i
j

Answers on page 64

Find analogue clock stickers to match each of these times.

6:40   9:10   2:15

PARENT TIP: Practise is needed when learning to tell the time. Children need to continue reading from analogue clocks even when they have digital watches and understand how the same time is shown on each. Work out time durations of films and TV programmes by counting on from start to end times.

53

Angles

Acute angle   Right angle   Obtuse angle

Help Jess to colour the acute angles yellow, the obtuse angles red and the right angles green.

Find some obtuse angles on the sticker sheet and put them here.

Circle the acute angles in these shapes.

PARENT TIP: Go on an angle hunt. Look around the house for different types of angles. Make a right angle tester by tearing off the corner of a sheet of paper and use it to check the angles. An angle smaller than the square corner is an acute angle, bigger means it is obtuse. Show your findings on a bar graph. Which type of angle did you see the most of?

54

Lines

Aaron has forgotten to use coloured lines when drawing his picture.

Use a ruler and felt-tip pens to draw over the lines using the correct colours.

_____ green
(horizontal)

| blue
(vertical)

_____ red
_____ (parallel)

Help Aaron find his way through the maze from **a** to **b** using horizontal and vertical lines. Draw lines to mark his pathway.

Count the number of each type of line that you have used.

Horizontal =

Vertical =

Could you have done it using fewer lines?

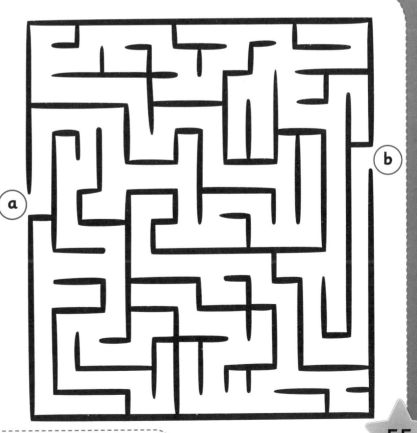

Division

Ben the greengrocer is sorting the fruit and vegetables into small groups. Help by circling the groups and calculating the answer.

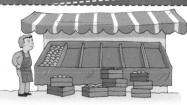

How many 3s in 12?

$12 \div 3 =$ ☐

How many 2s in 14?

$14 \div 2 =$ ☐

How many 4s in 20?

$20 \div 4 =$ ☐

How many 5s in 25?

$25 \div 5 =$ ☐

Complete some more divisions. Count up in steps to find the answer.

$21 \div 3 = 7$

$32 \div 4 =$ ☐ $35 \div 5 =$ ☐

$16 \div 4 =$ ☐ $18 \div 2 =$ ☐

$24 \div 4 =$ ☐ $15 \div 3 =$ ☐

How many 3s in 21?
3, 6, 9, 12, 15, 18, 21...
There are seven
3s in 21!

Answers on page 64

PARENT TIP: Help your child to read divisions as "how many __ in __?" This helps them to understand grouping. Practise counting up in steps of 2, 3, 4 and 5 to support this process. Links with multiplication facts are also very useful, so 7 x 3 = 21 and we know that 21 ÷ 3 = 7.

Ben puts up some posters to help when he sorts the fruit into groups.

Look at the number triangles below. Write two multiplication sentences and two division sentences that use the 3 numbers on the triangle.

E.g.

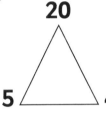

5 x 4 = 20	4 x 5 = 20
20 ÷ 4 = 5	20 ÷ 5 = 4

a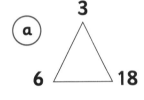

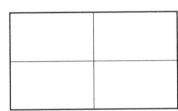

b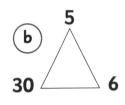

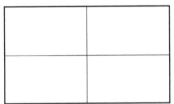

c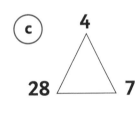

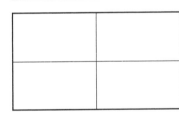

d

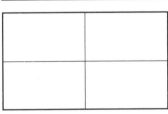

Ben discovers that some of the groupings cannot use up all the fruit.

Solve these divisions, then circle those with a remainder of 2.

a) 17 ÷ 5 = ⬚ r ⬚   b) 9 ÷ 2 = ⬚ r ⬚

c) 28 ÷ 3 = ⬚ r ⬚   d) 22 ÷ 4 = ⬚ r ⬚

e) 42 ÷ 10 = ⬚ r ⬚

Answers on page 64

More Fractions

Peter and Molly have some fraction tasks to do. They need you to help them write the equivalent fractions for these pairs of shapes. Work out these fractions. The first one has been done for you.

$$\frac{1}{4} \qquad \frac{2}{8}$$

Place the fraction stickers from the sticker sheet below in order of size.

Write the missing fractions in the boxes to complete the sequence.

$$\frac{1}{10}, \frac{2}{10}, \boxed{}, \boxed{}, \frac{5}{10}, \boxed{}, \frac{7}{10}, \boxed{}, \boxed{}, \frac{10}{10}$$

Circle the fraction above that is equal to $\frac{1}{2}$.

Answer on page 64

The fractions in the two boxes below have lost their partners.
Use the fraction wall to help you join pairs of equivalent fractions.

1											
$\frac{1}{2}$						$\frac{1}{2}$					
$\frac{1}{3}$			$\frac{1}{3}$				$\frac{1}{3}$				
$\frac{1}{4}$			$\frac{1}{4}$			$\frac{1}{4}$			$\frac{1}{4}$		
$\frac{1}{6}$		$\frac{1}{6}$		$\frac{1}{6}$		$\frac{1}{6}$		$\frac{1}{6}$		$\frac{1}{6}$	
$\frac{1}{12}$	$\frac{1}{12}$	$\frac{1}{12}$	$\frac{1}{12}$	$\frac{1}{12}$	$\frac{1}{12}$	$\frac{1}{12}$	$\frac{1}{12}$	$\frac{1}{12}$	$\frac{1}{12}$	$\frac{1}{12}$	$\frac{1}{12}$

Box 1:
$\frac{1}{3}$ $\frac{1}{6}$ $\frac{3}{4}$

$\left(\frac{2}{6}\right)$ $\frac{1}{2}$ $\frac{3}{12}$

Box 2:
$\frac{1}{4}$ $\frac{2}{12}$ $\frac{2}{4}$

$\frac{4}{12}$ $\frac{9}{12}$ $\left(\frac{1}{3}\right)$

Think up 4 other equivalent fraction pairs.

⬜ ⬜   ⬜ ⬜   ⬜ ⬜   ⬜ ⬜

Find answers of these fraction calculations:

$\frac{2}{3}$ of 6 = ⬜ $\frac{3}{4}$ of 8 = ⬜ $\frac{4}{5}$ of 15 = ⬜

Answers on page 64

PARENT TIP: Use buttons or pieces of pasta to help your child split quantities into fractions, e.g. to find 4/5 of 15, get 15 buttons and share into 5 groups explaining that each group is 1/5. Now push 4 of those groups together to create 4/5. Count the buttons to find 4/5 of 15.

Money

Mr Zandini runs the travelling circus. There are acrobats, clowns and fire jugglers. People pay to watch the show.

Here are the costs:

	Front rows	Side rows	Back rows
Adult	£3.50	£3.00	£2.50
Child	£2.50	£2.00	£1.50

Calculate the total cost and change needed for the families below.

a

We want seats at the side please.

Total Cost = _____
Change from £10.00 = _____

b

We want seats at the front please.

Total Cost = _____
Change from £10.00 = _____

c

We want seats at the back please.

Total Cost = _____
Change from £10.00 = _____

d

We want seats at the front please.

Total Cost = _____
Change from £20.00 = _____

Calculate the total cost for your family to go to the show. Compare the cost for each of the 3 seating positions. Which seats will you choose?

Answers on page 64

The ice cream seller has run out of change. His customers must pay with the exact money. Help these people choose which coins to pay with by circling them.

Need to pay £3.20

Need to pay £4.50

Need to pay £2.75

The prices of some of the snacks have been reduced. Calculate the new prices and find the new price sticker.

Popcorn	£3.75	£1.50 off	
Choc bar	99p	10p off	
Water	£1.00	15p off	
Fizzy pop	£1.50	20p off	
Crisps	80p	5p off	
Hot dog	£2.25	75p off	

Answers on page 64

PARENT TIP: Play 'how many ways?' Choose a money amount (e.g. £2.75) and find different ways to make the exact total using coins. Or you can play as a competition. The first to make the total wins.

61

Data Handling

Zak the zookeeper is delivering food to some of the animal enclosures.

He has put the food required onto trolleys in the warehouse.

Complete the table to help Zak record the food that has been used today.

	Tins	Bottles	Boxes	Bags
Lions	5	2	3	4
Penguins				
Elephants				
Monkeys				
TOTAL				

Which type of food has been used the most today: tins, bottles,

boxes or bags? _____

How many tins were used? _____

Of which food type were 8 used? _____

How many fewer bottles than boxes were used? _____

Answers on page 64

Zak checks the number of animals in each enclosure to make sure none have escaped. He records the results in a bar chart.

Bar chart: "number of animals" (y-axis, scale 0 to 24) vs "type of animal" (x-axis: lions, penguins, elephants, monkeys, meerkats, snakes)
- lions: 6
- penguins: 14
- elephants: 8
- monkeys: 8

How many monkeys are there? ....

Calculate the number of lions and elephants. ....

How many more penguins than lions are there? ....

Zak also counted 16 meerkats and 11 snakes. Add this information to the bar chart by colouring bars for the meerkats and for the snakes. Find the meerkat and snake stickers and put them here.

How many animals in total did Zak count? ....

Answers on page 64

63

Answers

Page 34: Numbers to 1000
1 - c, 2 - b, 3 - e, 4 - a, 5 - d
Flight 358 = three hundred and fifty-eight
Flight 721 = seven hundred and twenty-one
Flight 402 = four hundred and two
Flight 630 = six hundred and thirty

Page 35: 10 and 100
EJ529 = 625 mins, AA372 = 731 mins, SB843 = 884 mins, KG654 = 89 mins, BP459 = 228 mins, GP674 = 235 mins, FR328 = 373 mins

−100 from START time	−10 from START time	START	+10 from START time	+100 from START time
548	638	648	658	748

Page 36: Order Numbers to 1000
126 - 250 - 391 - 398 - 432 - 520 - 567 - 872
a = 383, b = 653, c = 492, d = 565, e = 279, f = 739

Page 37: Place Value to 1000
scales b = 700g + 50g + 3g / scales c = 400g + 80 g + 2g
479 = 400 + 70 + 9, 372 = 300 + 70 + 2,
600 + 20 + 3 = 623, 500 + 40 + 6 = 546

Page 38: Adding Numbers
yellow diver = tank c, blue diver = tank d,
purple diver = tank a, orange diver = tank b
a: 482 + 4 = 486
b: 546 + 30 = 576
c: 639 + 200 = 839
d: 257 + 40 = 297

Page 39: Adding Numbers (continued)
bass + cod: 352 + 521 = 873
turbot + ray: 622 + 215 = 837
cod + sole: 521 + 133 = 654
eel + ray: 476 + 215 = 691
1: turbot   2: sole   3: 101

Page 40: Perimeters
Field 2: 50m, Field 3: 60m, Field 4: 125m, Field 5: 100m

Page 41: Perimeters (continued)
Farmer Ted could fix field 1 and 3 or 1 and 2.
Farmer Ted needs to order 275m of fencing.

Page 42: Pictograms
Paper: 30 boxes, Glass: 15 boxes, Plastic: 40 boxes,
Cardboard: 20 boxes, Cans: 10 boxes. Plastic was collected the most.
15 boxes of glass were collected. 20 boxes more paper than cans.
20 boxes of cardboard were collected.

Page 43: Time Durations
Fishpool Street: Time taken is 30 mins, Driftwood Close: Time taken is 45 mins, Boundary Road: Time taken 15 mins. Mersey Way is finished at 20 minutes past 12. Driftwood Close took the longest to collect from. Total time = 3 hours 20 minutes

Page 44: Subtracting Numbers
657 bricks left, 826 tiles left, 384 metres of pipe left,
139 switches left, 293 litres of paint left

Page 45: Subtracting Numbers (continued)
There are 214 nails left at the end of the week.

Page 46: Fractions
a = 3/4, b = 4/5, c = 2/3, d = 5/7, e = 5/6, f = 6/8

Page 47: Fractions (continued)
Pirate a wants 4 gold coins, Pirate b wants 6 gold coins,
Pirate c wants 3 gold coins.
There isn't enough to give them all what they want.

Page 48: Multiply by 3, 4 and 8
18 bulbs in total. / Customer 1 = 6 bulbs, Customer 2 = 9 bulbs,
Customer 3 = 18 bulbs, Customer 4 = 15 bulbs / 12 bolts and 20 nuts.

Page 49: Multiply by 3, 4 and 8 (continued)
Tuesday = 12 tyres, Wednesday = 32 tyres, Thursday = 16 tyres,
Friday = 20 tyres / 28 spark plugs, 48 spark plugs / 3 x 8 = 24,
6 x 8 = 48, 4 x 8 = 32, 5 x 8 = 40, 7 x 8 = 56, 9 x 8 = 72

Page 50: Measures
crater a = 3m, crater b = 4.25m, crater c = 1.7m, crater d = 2.65m, crater e = 2.5m, Crater b is the widest. rock a = 2.75kg, rock b = 2kg, rock c = 1.5 kg. Rock a is the heaviest.

Page 51: Measures (continued)
a = 61cm, b = 57cm, c= 184cm, d = 265cm, e = 400cm, f = 89cm
Jug 1 = 450ml, jug 2 = 250ml, jug 3 = 850ml
jug 3 - jug 1 = 400ml, jug 1 - jug 2 = 200ml

Page 52: Multiplication
b = 68 cattle, c = 68 cattle, d = 120 cattle
2 day trip = 52 litres, 4 day trip = 104 litres, 8 day trip = 208 litres

Page 53: Analogue and Digital
a - i, b - e, c - j, d - g, f - h

Page 55: Lines
horizontal lines = 18, vertical lines = 19

Page 56: Division
12 ÷ 3 = 4, 14 ÷ 2 = 7, 20 ÷ 4 = 5, 25 ÷ 5 = 5, 21 ÷ 3 = 7,
32 ÷ 4 = 8, 35 ÷ 5 = 7, 16 ÷ 4 = 4, 18 ÷ 2 = 9, 24 ÷ 4 = 6, 15 ÷ 3 = 5

Page 57: Division (continued)
triangle a: 6 x 3 = 18, 3 x 6 = 18, 18 ÷ 3 = 6, 18 ÷ 6 = 3
triangle b: 5 x 6 = 30, 6 x 5 = 30, 30 ÷ 5 = 6, 30 ÷ 6 = 5
triangle c: 4 x 7 = 28, 7 x 4 = 28, 28 ÷ 4 = 7, 28 ÷ 7 = 4
triangle d: 2 x 8 = 16, 8 x 2 = 16, 16 ÷ 2 = 8, 16 ÷ 8 = 2
sums a, d and e have remainders of 2.
17 ÷ 5 = 3 r 2 / 9 ÷ 2 = 4 r 1 / 28 ÷ 3 = 9 r 1 /
22 ÷ 4 = 5 r 2 / 42 ÷ 10 = 4 r 2

Page 58: More Fractions
5/10 = 1/2

Page 59: More Fractions (continued)
2/3 of 6 = 4, 3/4 of 8 = 6, 4/5 of 15 = 12

Page 60: Money
Family a = £9 (£1 change), Family b = £9.50 (50p change),
Family c = £8 (£2 change), Family d = £17 (£3 change)

Page 61: Money (continued)
Popcorn = £2.25, Choc bar = 89p, Water = 85p,
Fizzy pop = £1.30, Crisps = 75p, Hot dog = £1.50

Page 62: Data Handling
Boxes have been used the most, 9 tins were used,
8 bags were used, 5 fewer bottles than boxes were used.

Page 63: Data Handling (continued)
8 monkeys / 14 lions and elephants / 8 / 63 animals

Leap Ahead
BUMPER
Workbook

ENGLISH

Home learning made FUN!

Speaking clearly

Decide which child is speaking correctly using standard English and cross out the incorrect speech bubbles. Remember, verbs like *seen* and *done* usually follow the verb *have*. For example, *he has seen* or *they have done*.

(a) I seen an orange balloon in the sky.

(b) I saw an orange balloon in the sky.

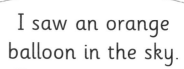

(c) My friend Sam done a bike race last week.

(d) My friend Sam did a bike race last week.

(e) We was so busy, we didn't realise the time!

(f) We were so busy, we didn't realise the time!

(g) I love those sweets. They are my favourite.

(h) I love them sweets. They are my favourite.

66

Answers on page 96

Past tense

Choose the correct verb forms to make the recount make sense.

Past progressive	Past simple	Present perfect
were hopping was running were trying were running was hopping	ran were was run had jumped	had walked have jumped has jumped

Fun at trampoline world!

At the weekend, Charlie and Archie went to the brand new Trampoline World. They .... so excited to visit because Charlie's cousin said it had 27 trampolines! They .... up and down with excitement as they entered the building. Archie didn't realise he .... into the exit door and couldn't get in! After collecting new lime green socks at the counter, the boys .... quickly through the corridor to start their bounce session.

Charlie shouted, "I .... over two trampolines, come and watch me!"

Soon, the boys .... all sorts of stunts and jumps. They .... a great time.

Answers on page 96

PARENT TIP: Past progressive tense uses the verb *to be* plus the *ing* form of the second verb in the chain (e.g. *he was jumping* or *they were jumping*). Write out some sentences for your child with a space for them to write was or were (e.g. *she ____ walking / the two boys ____ reading / the old lady ____ shopping / the children ____ writing*).

67

Plural or possessive?

"Plural" means "more than one". When we make a noun plural, we usually add an *s* to the word. For example: *one cat* changes to *two cats*.

We also add an *s* at the end of a word when something belongs to someone. With these, we also use an apostrophe. For example, *Jenny's coat*, *the dog's tail*.

Can you work out when to use plurals or possessives? Tick the boxes next to the correct words.

The lady is looking after the ☐ baby's.
☐ babies.

Yesterday, ☐ Tom's ☐ Toms school shoes went missing.

Can you collect the ☐ books ☐ book's in please?

The ☐ trousers ☐ trouser's were too long.

The ☐ spots ☐ spot's were all over the ☐ leopards ☐ leopard's legs.

Answers on page 96

Vowels and consonants

The hungry shark only eats vowels! Draw a line from jellyfish to jellyfish to lead the shark to his cave, eating 12 vowels along the way. Remember to avoid any consonants. Vowels are *a e i o u*. Consonants are the rest of the letters in the alphabet (*b c d f g h j k l m n p q r s t v w x y z*).

Answers on page 96

Find a sticker to match each word. Draw a circle around the vowels in each word. Which word has the most vowels? Put a tick next to it.

place sticker here	bike
place sticker here	circle
place sticker here	heart

place sticker here	potatoes
place sticker here	fruit
place sticker here	island

Expanded noun phrases

Expanded noun phrases give clear descriptions using adjectives and preposition phrases. Design and draw your own superhero in the box below, then label the features using expanded noun phrases. For example, *lightweight, black cape on his back*. When you design your superhero, think about their clothes and special powers.

Create a character card with a picture and description. Use expanded noun phrases to describe your superhero. Then add rankings by writing what your superhero does (e.g. *flying* or *running*) and colouring in the stars depending on how good your superhero is at each thing.

SUPERHERO:

DESCRIPTION:

....

....

....

RANKING:

....

....

....

....

....

....

....

Fronted adverbials

Fronted adverbials tell you the time, place or manner of what is happening in a sentence. They are used to link one sentence to another. Underline all the fronted adverbials in the text about an ice cream shop below. Then sort them into the table under the correct heading. Two have been done for you.

Every day, the ice cream shop opens for business. On the promenade, it stands out from all the other shops because of its large ice cream sign.

Inside the shop, an array of colours hits you and attacks your senses. Carefully, the ice cream seller sets out each flavour in a rainbow assortment. A row of forty flavours stretches from one end of the shop to the other. In the long freezers, the flavours range from toffee to bubblegum. After lunch, a queue forms at the door of excited children and adults waiting to choose their flavour. Noisily, the children shuffle forward to select an ice cream. Which one to choose?

Time	Place	Manner
After lunch		Noisily

Can you add any more fronted adverbials of your own to the table?

Answers on page 96

Starting a paragraph

New paragraphs often start with a fronted adverbial to introduce a new time, place, person or event.

Match the stickers on the sticker sheet to the correct sentences to show whether the fronted adverbial is introducing a time, place, person or event.

[place sticker here] Last night, there was a terrible storm.

[place sticker here] Over the hill, a rainbow appeared.

[place sticker here] In the hutch, the guinea pig snuggled up.

[place sticker here] Cautiously, the girl crept down the alley.

[place sticker here] Crash! Thunderously, the bridge collapsed at the start of the earthquake.

[place sticker here] Silently, the dark, cloaked figure crept across the hall.

[place sticker here] Suddenly, the teacher appeared from outside the classroom.

[place sticker here] After several minutes, the train left from platform 4b.

73

Answers on page 96

Castle poems

Read the poem about the medieval forest and underline any fronted adverbials. Practise saying the poem aloud. Can you rehearse it and perform it out loud to your family or friends?

The Medieval Forest

Across the meadow, the tall trees towered.

Next to each other, standing like a regiment of soldiers.

In the undergrowth, the animals scurried.

Around them, crinkling, crunching noises sounded.

Beside the evergreen forest stood a castle.

Up above, its turrets ascended.

The castle, their protector.

Look at this zoomed-in picture of the castle. Can you see its turrets, drawbridge, arrow slits and portcullis? Create your own poem to describe the castle. Describe where the features are using fronted adverbials.

The Castle

....

....

....

....

....

....

....

....

....

....

Ending in *sion* or *tion*?

Read the story and look out for the scrambled up words causing confusion. Rearrange the letters to make words ending in either *sion* or *tion*, and write the correct word above each anagram.

Deep in the castle, the king had a sniiov.

He pictured an army attacking the castle and

causing fcosinnou. Before meeting his soldiers, the

king made a esdnicoi. They would not sit back and

wait for the soivnain. In ratpreniopa for the attack, he made a plan

of noicat. He decided it was time to tell his men. When he reached

the top of the castle to meet the soldiers, an awful sight met him —

his soldiers were suffering from a serious nnctiofei!

Add the sticker *sion* or *tion* from the sticker sheet at the end of each group of letters to spell the words correctly.

inva   *place sticker here*   prepara   *place sticker here*

confu   *place sticker here*   deci   *place sticker here*

infec   *place sticker here*   collec   *place sticker here*

vi   *place sticker here*   cau   *place sticker here*

ac   *place sticker here*   preci   *place sticker here*

Answers on page 96

Super sentences

Some sentences have two clauses: a main clause and a subordinate clause (which starts with a subordinating conjunction). You can swap the main clause and subordinate clause around.

The players wear their stripy kit when they play at home.

can be changed to

When they play at home, the players wear their stripy kit.

Rewrite the sentences below, swapping the clauses around. Remember to change where the capital letter and full stop are.

The starting whistle blew when the players were ready.

....

....

Everyone slipped around because it was so muddy.

....

....

The crowd cheered loudly if their team scored.

....

....

Now create a sentence of your own. Choose from these conjunctions: that, although, as, while, because, if, when, before, after.

....

....

Answers on page 96

Apostrophes

Match up the stickers on the sticker sheet with the correct sentences, then put the apostrophe in the correct place to make a possessive word. The first apostrophe has been done for you.

place sticker here	The baby's toys.
place sticker here	The footballers boots.
place sticker here	The knights helmet.
place sticker here	The firefighters hose.
place sticker here	The teachers books.

Answers on page 96

PARENT TIP: When the plural ends in *s*, the apostrophe comes after the *s*, e.g. *the boys' cloakroom*. If the word is an irregular plural without *s* at the end, the apostrophe comes before the *s*, e.g. *the children's books*.

Spelling word search

It is easy to confuse words that end with the suffix *ture* or *sure*. Can you find the words in the box in this word search? Put a tick next to each one once you've found it.

t	c	g	v	u	r	k	h	p	r	n	p
r	b	l	q	n	h	c	k	l	o	c	m
e	j	f	t	a	y	g	m	e	z	j	e
a	q	o	f	t	b	z	x	a	a	c	a
s	u	z	a	u	d	v	u	s	j	r	s
u	x	f	u	r	n	i	t	u	r	e	u
r	e	k	v	e	h	c	l	r	k	a	r
e	n	c	l	o	s	u	r	e	b	t	e
g	x	a	d	p	j	y	q	v	g	u	b
b	m	f	p	i	c	t	u	r	e	r	a
i	k	a	d	v	e	n	t	u	r	e	h

treasure   enclosure   pleasure

furniture   creature   adventure

measure   nature   picture

Answers on page 96

Nouns and pronouns

Look at these children having a great time on the high ropes.
Write six sentences about what the children are doing using different
nouns and pronouns to talk about them (e.g. *the children, they, the kids,
the group*). The first sentence has been written for you.

> **Top tip!**
> When writing,
> try not to repeat
> the same noun
> or pronoun.
> It makes it boring
> for the reader.

The kids are running along the rickety wooden bridge.

You're becoming a fronted adverbial expert!

Look at this example sentence:
On top of the high rope, the children balanced carefully.

Add commas after fronted adverbials in these sentences:

From high in the sky the sun beamed down.

Cautiously the cat crept along the wall.

After lunch the children went out to play.

At sunset many swallows flew across the sky.

In the front room the children played their computer game.

Write a paragraph to describe a visit to an outdoor safari park.
Use fronted adverbials, commas and different nouns and pronouns.

....

....

....

....

....

....

....

....

....

....

Answers on page 96

Analysing text

Read the following story about a sleepover, then answer the questions about it on the next page.

The night had finally arrived! It was time for the sleepover. Lyra and Millie were very excited. Just after 5:00pm, they both arrived at Ruby's house and immediately changed into their pyjamas.

"Let's make cookies!" shouted Ruby. The three of them galloped down to the kitchen and rushed in to get ready to bake with big grins on their faces.

After an hour, a delicious smell was coming from the oven. They were busy playing party games and hadn't realised the cookies were ready until Ruby's dad called them. Huddling together on the bench, the friends ate one too many cookies and had to rub their tummies!

Bang! Pop! Guess what their next activity was? Balloon races! Everyone in the house was laughing and giggling... Everyone except Ruby's little cat, Fluff, who was cowering in the corner of the hall with her paws over her ears.

When it was time to settle down, ready for sleep, Lyra suggested they watch a film. The three buddies snuggled up together under a blanket and started watching the film trailers.

Suddenly, a loud click was heard and the house plunged into darkness. The only sound they could hear was Fluff meowing. "Oh no!" cried Ruby. "Not a power cut!"

(1) How many children were at the sleepover?

....

(2) How did the girls feel about baking?

....

....

(3) Why did the girls rub their tummies?

....

....

(4) Did Fluff enjoy the balloon games? How do you know?

....

....

(5) Find and copy a word that suggests the children sat closely together.

....

(6) How do you think the children felt after the power cut?

....

....

....

(7) What do you think happened next?

....

....

....

Answers on page 96

Determiners

A determiner is a word used before a noun to explain exactly what the noun is referring to. Common determiners are *the*, *a*, *these* and *many*. Choose an appropriate determiner sticker and noun sticker from the sticker sheet to match the picture.

a (place sticker here) (place sticker here)

b (place sticker here) (place sticker here)

c (place sticker here) (place sticker here)

d (place sticker here) (place sticker here)

e (place sticker here) (place sticker here)

f (place sticker here) (place sticker here)

Write a sentence using determiners and nouns.

....

....

....

....

84

Answers on page 96

Curious spellings

Complete the crossword with words that end in *ous* using the clues in the box below. Some letters have already been added to help you.

ACROSS
1 - A person who asks questions
2 - An elephant compared to a mouse is...
3 - Another word for 'many'
4 - When something bad happens, it is...
5 - A happy person is often...

DOWN
1 - A snake with venom is...
2 - A well-known celebrity is...
3 - Someone who is very brave

Answers on page 96

What do you notice about the spellings?

....

Can you find a rule?

....

85

Using direct speech

Read through the following conversations.

(a)

I've lost my dog! Can you help?

When did you last see it?

(b)

Please can I have some sweets? I have 50p.

Yes. I'll do you a mixed bag.

(c)

Look out! There's a rock on the road there.

Don't worry. I've seen it! I'll skate around it.

Top tip: there are five rules for writing direct speech correctly.

1. You need a comma after a reporting clause.
2. Spoken words are written inside a pair of inverted commas: "___".
3. A capital letter should be used at the start of speech.
4. Use a comma inside the inverted commas if your sentence carries on after the speech has finished.
5. Each new speaker needs a new line.

Now write the speech from the speech bubbles into direct speech below. Remember to use the five rules to write direct speech correctly. The first one has been done for you.

a) "I've lost my dog! Can you help?" asked the girl

b)

c)

Adverb exceptions

You can create adverbs from adjectives by adding the suffix *ly*. Sometimes, you have to modify the word using these rules:

1. If the word ends in y, change it to *i* (e.g. *snappy / snappily*).
2. Following *ic* add *ally* (e.g. *frantic / frantically*).
3. If a word ends in *le*, change the *e* to a *y* (e.g. *wiggle / wiggly*)
4. Just add *ly* to all the others.

Change the words below into adverbs using the rules.

(a) frantic ....

(b) happy ....

(c) gentle ....

(d) kind ....

(e) angry ....

(f) basic ....

(g) prickle ....

(h) merry ....

(i) classic ....

(j) cautious ....

(k) crazy ....

Choose an adverb from the list above and write a sentence using it.

....

....

....

Answers on page 96

Expanded noun phrases

Draw a new pet in the box below. It can be an imaginary pet or one made from the features of other pets. Think about its head, body, arms and legs, and if it has any other features such as claws, a tail or a beak.

Write expanded noun phrases to describe your pet. Make it sound like a great pet to have.

Persuasive writing

Imagine your pet is for sale in a pet shop. Design a poster to advertise your pet. Remember all the features of persuasive writing:

1. emotive language (e.g. you will never have a more loving pet)
2. clear descriptions using expanded noun phrases
3. questions
4. adverbs.

Your poster should have: a picture, the name and price of the pet, a detailed description about it and a paragraph about why someone should buy it.

Write a letter to your friend telling them all about the new pet, and persuade them to buy it. Use the persuasive writing features (listed on page 90) to make sure your letter contains the right details.

Proofreading

Read this recount about a trip to the museum. Proofread the writing to check if there are any spelling or punctuation mistakes. Change the mistakes with a coloured pen.

While proofreading, you should check for: capital letters and full stops, questions and exclamation marks, apostrophes for possession, commas after fronted adverbials, speech punctuation and spelling.

On thursday 1st March, Class 4 visited a museum, which was an hour away from their school

Once the teacher had taken the register the class lined up in pears to get on the coach. excited children chated all the way to the museum.

When they arrived, the teacher led them into the entrance hall and counted to check everywon was their. "Come on! he shouted. "We're off to the Ancient Greeks sechion!"

Wandering threw the museum, the children spotted vases and bowls like they had seen in class.

when it was time to leave, they had to collect the childrens coats from the cloakroom. What a fantastic trip it had been

Answers on page 96

Spelling practice

Can you spell all of these words? You have practised all the rules for them in this book. Ask an adult to test you or write out your spellings, then check them yourself.

prickly

caution

question

action

circle

happily

enormous

measure

famous

creature

future

vision

adventure

basically

Writing a recount

Use this page to plan a recount about the best day of your life.

Note down some ideas for each section using the bullet points.

Introduction (tell the reader about yourself using the present tense):

- ....
- ....
- ....
- ....

Best time in your life (describe people and places using the past tense):

- ....
- ....
- ....
- ....

Challenging time in your life (describe people/places using the past tense):

- ....
- ....
- ....
- ....

Summary (write about your hopes for the future using the future tense):

- ....
- ....
- ....
- ....

Write a blog post about the best day of your life in four paragraphs, following the plan you've created. Remember to use: fronted adverbials, direct speech for quotes, expanded noun phrases for description and correct punctuation.

← →

Answers

Page 66: Speaking clearly
The correct sentences are: b, d, f, g

Page 67: Past tense
were/were hopping/had walked/ran/jumped/were trying/had

Page 68: Plural or possessive?
babies / Tom's / books / trousers / spots / leopard's

Page 69: Vowels and consonants

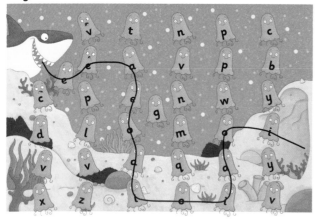

bike circle heart potatoes fruit island

Page 72: Fronted adverbials

Time	Place	Manner
After lunch Every day	Inside the shop On the promenade In the long freezers	Noisily Carefully

Page 73: Starting a paragraph
Time: Last night, there was a terrible storm.
After several minutes, the train left from platform 4b.
Suddenly, the teacher appeared from outside the classroom.
Place: In the hutch, the guinea pig snuggled up.
Over the hill, a rainbow appeared.
Person: Cautiously, the girl crept down the alley.
Silently, the dark, cloaked figure crept across the hall.
Event: Crash! Thunderously, the bridge collapsed at the start of the attack.

Page 76: Ending in *sion* or *tion*?
vision / confusion / decision / invasion / preparation / action / infection
Endings: invasion, confusion, infection, vision, action, preparation, decision, collection, caution, precision

Page 77: Super sentences
When the players were ready, the starting whistle blew.
Because it was so muddy, everyone slipped around.
If their team scored, the crowd cheered loudly.

Page 78: Apostrophes
baby's toys / footballers' boots / knight's helmet / firefighters' hose / teachers' books

Page 79: Spelling word search

t	c	g	v	u	r	k	h	p	r	n	p
r	b	l	q	n	h	c	k	l	o	c	m
e	j	f	t	a	y	g	m	e	z	j	e
a	q	o	f	t	b	z	x	a	a	c	a
s	u	z	a	u	d	v	u	s	j	r	s
u	x	f	u	r	n	i	t	u	r	e	u
r	e	k	v	e	h	c	l	r	k	a	r
e	n	c	l	o	s	u	r	e	b	t	e
g	x	a	d	p	j	y	q	v	g	u	b
b	m	f	p	i	c	t	u	r	e	r	a
i	k	a	d	v	e	n	t	u	r	e	h

Page 81: Nouns and pronouns
From high in the sky, the sun beamed down.
Cautiously, the cat crept along the wall.
After lunch, the children went out to play.
At sunset, many swallows flew across the sky.
In the front room, the children played their computer game.

Page 83: Analysing text
1. Three. 2. Excited/happy. 3. They had eaten too many cookies. 4. No, Fluff was scared. We know this because she was hiding in the corner of the hall with her paws covering her ears. 5. snuggled 6. scared, nervous, worried 7. (no single correct answer for this question.)

Page 84: Determiners
Various possible answers, e.g. a) The children b) That dog c) Two eyes d) His diary e) A phone f) Many people

Page 85: Curious spellings
1 across: curious   4 across: disastrous 2 down: famous
2 across: enormous 5 across: joyous   3 down: courageous
3 across: various   1 down: poisonous

Page 87: Using direct speech
a) "I've lost my dog! Can you help?" asked the girl.
"When did you last see it?" replied the police officer.
b) "Please can I have some sweets? I have 50p," explained the boy.
"Yes. I'll do you a mixed bag," said the shopkeeper.
c) "Look out! There's a rock on the road there," shouted the skater to his friend.
"Don't worry. I've seen it! I'll skate around it," the other skater shouted back.

Page 88: Adverb exceptions
a) frantically b) happily c) gently d) kindly e) angrily f) basically g) prickly h) merrily i) classically j) cautiously k) crazily

Page 92: Proofreading
On **T**hursday 1st March, Class 4 visited a museum, which was an hour away from their school**.** Once the teacher had taken the register, the class lined up in **pairs** to get on the coach. **E**xcited children chat**t**ed all the way to the museum. When they arrived, the teacher led them into the entrance hall and counted to check every**one** was the**re**. "Come on**!**" he shouted. "We're off to the Ancient Greeks sec**t**ion!" Wandering **through** the museum, the children spotted vases and bowls like they had seen in class. **W**hen it was time to leave, they had to collect the children's coats from the cloakroom. What a fantastic trip it had been**.**

Leap Ahead
BUMPER
Workbook

MATHS

Home learning made FUN!

Reading and comparing

Four friends are competing on the television game show *Friends of Fortune*. Their podiums show their winnings at the end of Round 1. Write each contestant's winnings in words. Steve's is done for you.

Steve £1807

Jenny £3050

Mike £2246

Alice £1355

One thousand, eight hundred and seven

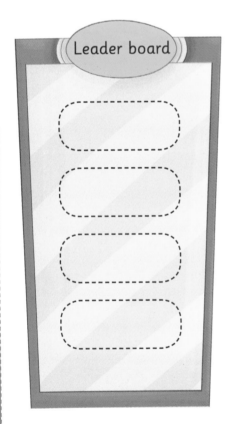

Leader board

Now put the contestants in order on the leader board, using the four names on the sticker sheet. Put the person with the most money at the top and the person with the least money at the bottom.

At the end of Round 2, Alice has won £2000, Jenny has lost £500, Mike has lost £90 and Steve has won £800. Write everyone's new totals after Round 2.

Alice ....

Jenny ....

Mike ....

Steve ....

Answers on page 128

The scores below show how much money the players had won by the end of Round 3. In Round 4, players win or lose multiples of £100. Based on this, answer the questions below.

ROUND 3 SCORES

Alice: £5435   Jenny: £3930   Mike: £5859   Steve: £4518

(a) How much money does Alice need to win to take the lead?

....

(b) How much does Jenny need to win to catch up with Steve?

....

(c) How much does Mike need to win to pass his target of £6500?

....

The computer system has got a virus which is causing the contestants' winnings for Round 5 to be calculated incorrectly. Explain the mistake for each contestant, and write the correct answer below.

	Round 4 scores	Amount won or lost in Round 5	New score
Alice	£6560	Lost £500	£7060
Jenny	£3546	Won £300	£6546
Mike	£7355	Won £50	£7395
Steve	£4290	Won £800	£4090

Alice: ....

Jenny: ....

Mike: ....

Steve: ....

Answers on page 128

PARENT TIP: When your child walks up and down the stairs, encourage them to count in different multiples of 10 and 100 from different starting points. For example, start at 345 and count in 200s, or start at 840 and count backwards in multiples of 30.

Rounding

This table shows the visitor numbers for the first 6 months at a new trampoline park. Complete the table by rounding the numbers for each month to the nearest 10, 100 and 1000.

	Visitor numbers	Rounded to the nearest 10	Rounded to the nearest 100	Rounded to the nearest 1000
January	2345			
February	2767			
March	3698			
April	3064			
May	4002			
June	2986			

For July, August and September, the manager Sue has got the visitor numbers in a muddle because they all contain the same four digits: 2, 3, 6, 8. Can you work out what the visitor numbers were for each month, using Sue's rounded numbers?

	Visitor numbers	Rounded to nearest 10	Rounded to nearest 100	Rounded to nearest 1000
July		2860	2900	3000
August		2640	2600	3000
September		3270	3300	3000

Answers on page 128

(a) Sue works out the visitor numbers for the rest of the year. First, she rounds the visitor numbers for October to 2300 to the nearest hundred. What could the number of visitors have been? Give three possibilities.

....

(b) What are the highest and lowest possible visitor numbers?

Highest ....   Lowest ....

(c) She forgot to add a birthday party to October's numbers. Including the birthday party, October's number rounds to 2400 to the nearest hundred. What are the highest and lowest visitor numbers there could have been in October?

Highest ....   Lowest ....

(d) In November, the number of visitors was 3966. Round this number to the nearest 100 and nearest 1000. What do you notice?

....

....

(e) In December, there were 7203 visitors. Sue says that 7203 to the nearest 10 is 7200 but she is confused because this is a multiple of 100. Can you help her understand?

....

....

(f) Sue says that if she had had one more visitor in January, the number would have rounded to 9000 to the nearest 1000. How many visitors did she have?

....

Answers on page 128

101

Adding 4-digit numbers

These are the supporter numbers for two football teams at the first five football matches of the season. Complete the calculations to find out which match had the most supporters altogether.

Match	Team A	Team B
1	3264	2337
2	2189	1834
3	1976	2735
4	2823	1977
5	2028	3269

Match 1
```
  3264
+ 2337
_____

_____
```

Match 2
```
  2189
+ 1834
_____

_____
```

Match 3
```
  1976
+ 2735
_____

_____
```

Match 4
```
  2823
+ 1977
_____

_____
```

Match 5
```
  2028
+ 3269
_____

_____
```

The match with the most supporters was:

....

For one of the matches, Sam uses rounding to the nearest 100 to estimate that there were 4000 spectators in total. Which of the matches was he estimating and how do you know?

....

At another match, there are 2346 fans for the home team and 1629 fans for the away team. Sam says this is about 3900 people. His dad says it is about 4000. How did they arrive at different estimations?

....

....

....

....

Answers on page 128

These are the supporter numbers for the following three matches.
Complete the calculations then circle the team with the most supporters.

Match	Team A	Team B
6	2187	1793
7	1862	3436
8	3246	2058

Team A
```
  2187
  1862
+ 3246
_____

_____
```

Team B
```
  1793
  3436
+ 2058
_____

_____
```

Sam noticed there is some mud splattered over some of his workings for two of the matches. Can you work out the digits that are covered in mud? Use the correct stickers from your sticker sheet.

```
   2  7  ▓  5
+  ▓  4  4  ▓
_____
   4  ▓  1  3
```

```
   3  ▓  1  ▓
+  2  6  ▓  7
_____
   ▓  9  0  1
```

For the final match of the season, there are 1845 fans for team A and 1999 fans for team B. Dad says Sam could find the total spectators using a mental method. How could you do it mentally?

Answers on page 128

PARENT TIP: Get your child to throw a dice 8 times to make two 4 digit numbers, then add the two numbers together. Then ask them to try rearranging the digits to make two new 4 digit numbers. Can they make a bigger total than before?

Subtracting 4-digit numbers

The Bailey family are looking at holidays online. Below are the prices for a family of four to different locations:

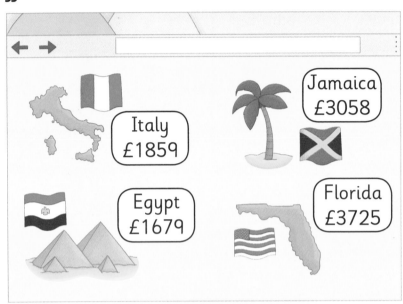

Italy £1859

Jamaica £3058

Egypt £1679

Florida £3725

They compare the prices using subtraction to find the difference. Can you help them? How much more expensive is:

(a) **Florida than Jamaica?**

```
  3725
- 3058
------

------
```

(b) **Jamaica than Italy?**

```
  3058
- 1859
------

------
```

(c) **Italy than Egypt?**

```
  1859
- 1679
------

------
```

(d) Mr Bailey has £1549 saved. How much more would he need to save to book a holiday to Jamaica? Fill in the boxes to complete the calculation.

☐ ☐ ☐ ☐
− ☐ ☐ ☐ ☐
☐ ☐ ☐ ☐

(e) The family have set a budget of £4500. How much would they have left to spend away if they went to Italy?

☐ ☐ ☐ ☐
− ☐ ☐ ☐ ☐
☐ ☐ ☐ ☐

Answers on page 128

The family have decided to go to Florida and have a budget of £2450 for excursions.

f) If they go to the theme park, how much will be left for other excursions?

```
   2450
 - 1265
 _____

 _____
```

Family ticket prices

Theme park pass	£1265
Sealife attraction	£189
Wildlife park	£248
Water park	£162
Film studios	£298
Space centre	£164
Dolphin encounter	£329

They pay for the theme park, then choose the other days out. How much will they have left after each trip? Use the remaining money each time.

g) Wildlife park   **h)** Space centre   **i)** Film studios   **j)** Dolphin encounter

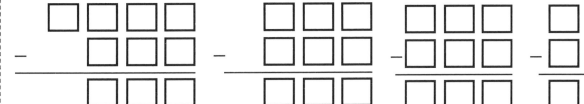

k) Do they have enough money left to visit the water park? Circle your answer.

y e s   /   n o

Mr Bailey compares the visitors to the Water park and the Wildlife park in January and July by finding the difference. He thinks he's made some mistakes so he uses addition to check. Complete his addition checks for him, then explain what he did wrong.

Wildlife park

January: 6325   July: 9164

Mr Bailey's working	Addition check
9164	6325
− 6325	+ 3241
3241	_____

Water park

January: 5126   July: 7823

Mr Bailey's working	Addition check
7823	5126
− 5126	+ 2703
2703	_____

Answers on page 128

Using times tables facts

Luke collects stickers and likes to arrange them by theme in his sticker album in arrays. He has 3 rows of 6 animal-themed stickers which he writes as 3 x 6.

3 x 6

He could have arranged his 18 stickers in different arrays. Use the stickers to complete two more arrays in this box, then label them with their multiplication facts.

Answers on page 128

Luke uses Factor Rainbows to help him find all the ways he could arrange the **60** stickers in his sticker album.

1 2 3 4 5 6   10 12 15 20 30 60

Luke gets 12 more stickers, making 72 stickers in total. Complete the factor rainbow to see how he could arrange them in his sticker album.

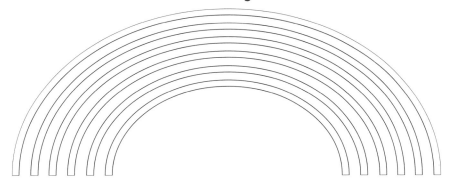

Luke and his friend Ella are comparing how many stickers they have. Write the correct symbol (>, < or =) to show who has more stickers in each theme.

(a) Football stickers

4 x 7 ☐ 8 x 3

(b) Dinosaur stickers

5 x 9 ☐ 9 x 7

(c) Space stickers

12 x 4 ☐ 8 x 6

Luke says that if 4 rows of 3 stickers is 12, then he can work out that 40 rows of 3 stickers is 120. Can you use your multiplication facts to help Luke work out how many stickers he would have on these pages?

6 0   x   7 = ...

5   x   3 0 0 = ...

2 0   x   8 0 = ...

Answers on page 128

Multiplying and dividing mentally

Captain Multivide has magical powers. Jack is putting them to the test!

I can multiply and divide any number by 10 or 100!

Complete the table for each number Jack gives Captain Multivide with what you think his answer will be.

Jack's number	Captain Multivide's power	New number
23	× 10	
17	÷ 100	
30	÷ 10	
16	× 100	
12	÷ 10	

Jack whispers his number to Captain Multivide and the Captain secretly carries out his power. Can you read Captain Multivide's mind and say what power he's using to change the number each time?

(a) 3.7 → 37

(b) 0.59 → 59

(c) 190 → 19

....

Answers on page 128

Something's gone wrong with Captain Multivide's power and all the answers are coming out wrong. Help him get his power back by telling him what he's done wrong.

Jack's number	Captain Multivide's power	New number	What was his mistake?
34	× 100	340	He multiplied by 10 instead of 100.
23	÷ 10	230	
72	× 10	7200	
20	÷ 100	2	
9	÷ 10	0.09	

Captain Multivide's super team mate, Captain Zerone, has powers of his own using 0 and 1. Can you predict his answers?

(d) 2 3 1 × 1 = ...

(e) 3 5 × 0 = ...

(f) 6 2 ÷ 1 = ...

(g) 5 6 0 × 1 = ...

(h) 9 9 ÷ 1 = ...

(i) 3 0 0 0 × 0 = ...

I think that when you multiply a number, it always gets bigger.

What would Captain Zerone say about Captain Multivide's theory? Write in his response.

....
....

Answers on page 128

Multiplying 3-digit numbers

Jackie is a long-distance lorry driver. She has 5 destinations she regularly travels to. She is wondering which destination has contributed the most miles to her milometer. Can you help her work it out?

Food factory 342 miles

Food shop 138 miles

DEPOT

Clothes shop 67 miles

Paper factory 239 miles

Offices 185 miles

This month, Jackie has driven to the food factory 5 times, the clothes shop 6 times, the paper factory 4 times, the food shop 9 times and the offices 7 times. Can you help her work out how many miles each destination has contributed to her total distance travelled?

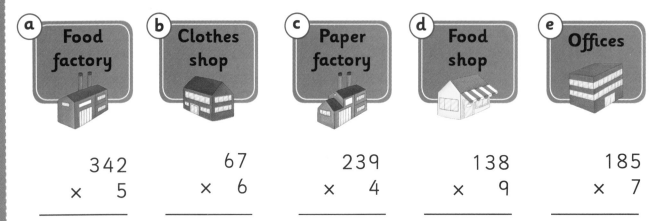

a **Food factory**

b **Clothes shop**

c **Paper factory**

d **Food shop**

e **Offices**

$$\begin{array}{r} 342 \\ \times \quad 5 \\ \hline \end{array}$$

$$\begin{array}{r} 67 \\ \times \quad 6 \\ \hline \end{array}$$

$$\begin{array}{r} 239 \\ \times \quad 4 \\ \hline \end{array}$$

$$\begin{array}{r} 138 \\ \times \quad 9 \\ \hline \end{array}$$

$$\begin{array}{r} 185 \\ \times \quad 7 \\ \hline \end{array}$$

Jackie has driven the most miles in total to ....

Answers on page 128

ⓕ Every time Jackie fills up with fuel, it costs £248 in petrol. Over a week, she fills up 6 times. How much does she spend on fuel? Use the box for your workings.

ⓖ Sometimes Jackie stays overnight in a hotel. The hotel costs £136 per night. This month, she stayed there 7 times. How much money did she spend on the hotel? Use the box for your workings.

Jackie gets paid different rates for different days. She works out her month's pay by multiplying the different day rates by the number of days she's worked at each rate, but she gets oily fingerprints over her workings. Use stickers to fill in the missing digits.

£235 per day for 8 days

£178 per day for 6 days

£186 per day for 5 days

```
    2 3 ■              ■ 7 8            1 ■ 6
  ×     8            ×     ■          ×     5
  _____            _____          _____
  1 ■ 8 0            1 0 6 8            9 3 ■
```

Answers on page 128

PARENT TIP: Take turns with your child to write out a multiplication calculation with a deliberate mistake. Can you and your child spot and explain the mistake you have made?

111

Equivalent fractions

Jeff and Alan are neighbours and have identical rectangular spaces in their gardens to plant vegetables.

Jeff   Alan

The two gardeners split up their vegetable patches into fractions. Write how much of their patch is taken up by each type of vegetable, giving the answer as a fraction in its simplest form.

a Jeff's carrots: ....

b Alan's potatoes: ....

c Jeff's tomatoes: ....

d Alan's tomatoes: ....

e Jeff says that he and Alan have the same fraction of tomatoes. Do you agree? Prove it. ....

....

f Alan says that cabbages take up $\frac{3}{12}$ of his patch. His partner says it is $\frac{1}{4}$. Who is right? ....

g Jeff says that they both have the same fraction of carrots because they both have 2 parts. Show that he is wrong using equivalent fractions.

....

....

112

Answers on page 128

Alan and Jeff's neighbour across the road, Sally, is planning her own vegetable patch.

Add the missing digits to show what fraction each type of vegetable takes up.

(h) Potatoes: $\dfrac{3}{}$ (i) Carrots: $\dfrac{}{4}$ (j) Tomatoes: $\dfrac{1}{}$

(k) Plan your own vegetable patch for this garden. Use stickers to fill the spaces matching the fractions below.

Potatoes: $\dfrac{2}{5}$ Carrots: $\dfrac{1}{4}$ Tomatoes: $\dfrac{1}{5}$

Cabbages: $\dfrac{1}{10}$ Radishes: $\dfrac{1}{20}$

Answers on page 128

PARENT TIP: When cooking, encourage your children to cut up ingredients in different fractional parts. Ask them to describe how they have cut the food up and how many parts have been taken. E.g. "I have cut the cake into eights. I'm having two pieces so that's a $\dfrac{1}{4}$."

Decimal numbers

Mrs Hanlon is making costumes for the school play. She has lots of fabric and ribbons to cut up. This is how much fabric she needs for each costume:

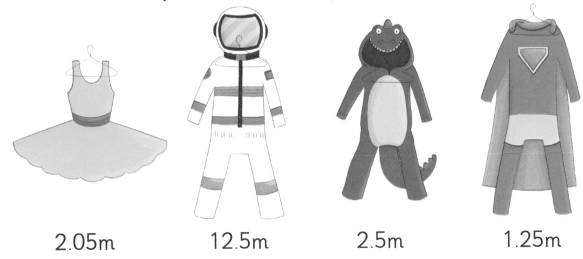

2.05m   12.5m   2.5m   1.25m

Put the costumes from the sticker sheet in order of the length of fabric needed, from least to most.

Her ribbons come in 1m lengths but her pattern gives her the fractions of 1m that she needs. Write the lengths she needs to cut as a decimal number.

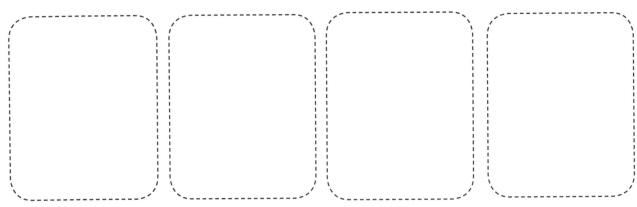

a $\frac{3}{10}$ of red ribbon = ... metres

b $\frac{25}{100}$ of blue ribbon = ... metres

c $\frac{7}{1000}$ of black ribbon = ... metres

Answers on page 128

d) Some children are helping Mrs Hanlon to cut the ribbons. Rebecca reads the instructions, "Cut $\frac{3}{10}$ of a 1m ribbon." She measures 0.03m and is surprised at how short the piece of ribbon is. What did she do wrong?

....

....

Match the decimal that Rebecca should measure to each of these fractions. You can find the decimal stickers on the sticker sheet.

$\frac{2}{100}$ ( ) $\frac{5}{10}$ ( )

$\frac{5}{100}$ ( ) $\frac{25}{100}$ ( )

$\frac{20}{100}$ ( ) $\frac{7}{100}$ ( )

Mrs Hanlon gives Rebecca some numbers to practise ordering. Can you help her choose the correct sign? Use the stickers on your sticker sheet.

$\frac{4}{10}$ ( ) 0.5 $\frac{8}{100}$ ( ) 0.08

0.53 ( ) 0.35   0.17 ( ) $\frac{2}{10}$

0.06 ( ) $\frac{6}{10}$ 0.5 ( ) $\frac{35}{100}$

Answers on page 128

PARENT TIP: Write some decimal numbers with one or two decimal places on sticky notes. Take turns to turn one over at a time. Whoever has the biggest number can keep it. Whoever collects the most numbers wins.

Fraction problems

To help pass the time while swimming, Sophie keeps track of the lengths she has swum as fractions.

On Monday, she plans to swim 40 lengths. How many lengths will she have swum after she has done:

(a) $\frac{1}{10}$ of her lengths? ....

(b) $\frac{5}{8}$ of her lengths? ....

(c) $\frac{3}{5}$ of her lengths? ....

(d) $\frac{3}{4}$ of her lengths? ....

(e) On Tuesday, she plans to swim 60 lengths. After 22 lengths, she says she has swum more than $\frac{1}{4}$ but less than $\frac{1}{2}$. Do you agree? Why?

....

....

(f) On Wednesday, she only has time to swim 30 lengths. After swimming for 15 minutes, she has swum $\frac{2}{5}$ of her total lengths. How many lengths has she swum?

....

....

(g) On Thursday, after swimming 18 lengths, she has swum $\frac{2}{5}$ of her total. How many lengths is she planning to swim?

....

....

Answers on page 128

(h) The following week, Sophie isn't feeling very well and stops swimming before completing her targeted lengths. How many lengths did she swim each day? On which day did she swim the most lengths?

Monday: $\frac{3}{4}$ of 48 lengths ....

Tuesday: $\frac{2}{3}$ of 60 lengths ....

Wednesday: $\frac{3}{8}$ of 80 lengths ....

Sophie swam the most lengths on: ....

(i) The next week, Sophie sets herself a goal of 100 lengths over the whole week. Work out what fraction of these she swam each day.

Monday: 25 lengths ....

Tuesday: 20 lengths ....

Wednesday: 10 lengths ....

Thursday: 30 lengths ....

Friday: 15 lengths ....

(j) Sophie swims 40 lengths on Saturday. She says that when she has swum $\frac{1}{3}$ of her total lengths, she will be part way through a lap. Do you agree? Why?

....

(k) Circle the fractions below that will be a complete number of lengths.

$\frac{1}{8}$ $\quad\quad\quad$ $\frac{2}{5}$ $\quad\quad\quad$ $\frac{1}{6}$ $\quad\quad\quad$ $\frac{3}{10}$ $\quad\quad\quad$ $\frac{4}{9}$

Answers on page 128

PARENT TIP: Ask your children, "Would you rather..." and give them two options to choose. For example, $\frac{2}{3}$ of this pile of 12 sweets or $\frac{1}{2}$ of this pile of 20 sweets? Would you rather have $\frac{3}{4}$ of 20 minutes on your tablet or $\frac{5}{6}$ of an hour?

Shape properties

Jake has been researching quadrilaterals on the internet. Can you match his search results to the correct shape? Write the correct letter next to the shapes below.

(a)
4 equal sides
2 pairs of equal angles
2 pairs of parallel sides
2 lines of symmetry

(b)
2 pairs of equal sides
4 right angles
2 lines of symmetry

(c)
2 pairs of equal sides
2 pairs of equal angles
2 pairs of parallel sides
0 lines of symmetry

(d)
4 equal sides
4 right angles
4 lines of symmetry

rhombus   equilateral   rectangle   square

○   ○   ○   ○

Jake has written out some properties of triangles, but he's missing some words. Can you fill them in? Use the images to help you.

(e) .... triangles have two equal sides and two equal angles.

(f) .... triangles have one right angle and two acute angles.

(g) .... triangles have all equal angles and all equal sides.

(h) .... triangles have no equal sides.

isosceles   right-angled   equilateral   scalene
triangle   triangle   triangle   triangle

118

Answers on page 128

Jake plays a game with his friend, Billy. He thinks of a shape and describes it to Billy. Billy guesses the shape, but there are two that he's stuck on. Can you help him? Fill in the empty speech bubbles.

(i) It has 4 sides and one line of symmetry. None of the sides are parallel.

....

(j) It has 4 sides and one pair of parallel sides.

....

Jake is wondering if it is always true, sometimes true or never true that...

k. ... quadrilaterals have 4 sides?

l. ... triangles have 2 obtuse angles?

m. ... quadrilaterals have right angles?

Write the answers below and explain why for each one.

k. ....

l. ....

m. ....

Answers on page 128

Angles

Alice has been learning about angles at school. She has been asked to find different angles around her home. She notices there are lots of angles on her bike. Can you help her identify which of these angles are obtuse and which are acute? Sort the angles into the table for her.

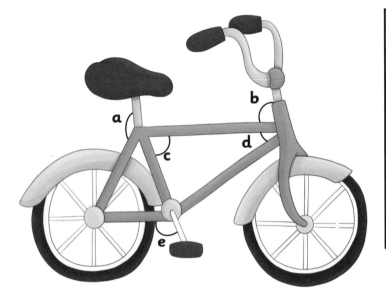

Acute	Obtuse

Alice has drawn a picture of her house and notices more angles. Can you identify them and sort them into the table?

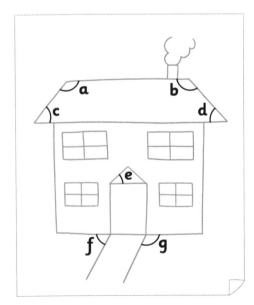

Acute	Obtuse

Answers on page 128

Alice notices that the hands of the clock form angles, too. Can you find the angle in degrees marked between the hands of each clock face?

Now use the clock stickers on the sticker sheet to place the angles in order of size from smallest to biggest.

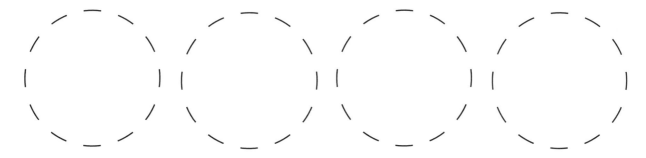

Alice plays a game with her brother. She tells him three facts about the angles inside different shapes and asks him which one is a fib. Can you spot the fib? Put a circle around it then explain why.

a A rectangle can never have an acute angle.

b A regular hexagon has only obtuse angles.

c All the angles of a rhombus are acute.

Answers on page 128

PARENT TIP: Pick up a pile of straws or kebab sticks and drop them on the table. Challenge your child to find as many different acute and obtuse angles between the sticks that cross over as they can. What are there more of, acute or obtuse?

Units of measure

Alex the astronaut is preparing for her journey into space. She needs to get all the supplies ready for the mission.

The table below shows the quantities of different freeze-dried foods Alex and her crew will need each day. Their mission will last 100 days. How many kilograms of each food should they take? Complete the table.

Food type	Daily quantity	Total in kg
Freeze-dried coffee	35g	
Powdered milk	120g	
Dehydrated vegetables	550g	
Dried biscuits	375g	
Heat-treated tortillas	200g	

(a) Alex estimates that they will need 250ml of lubricant every day to keep the space station's mechanisms working smoothly. How many litres will they need over the 100 day mission?

....

....

(b) The astronauts move around the space station a lot without gravity holding them down. Alex thinks she travels 350m every day. How far does she move each day in kilometres?

....

(c) The astronauts strap themselves down to sleep on their beds. Joe measures the width of his bed and says it is only 0.85m. How wide is this in cm?

....

Answers on page 128

Alex prefers decimal numbers and measures everything in larger units. Joe prefers whole numbers so he uses smaller units of measure. Can you match the equivalent measurements they have each made? The first one has been done for you.

0.06m	600g
0.6m	6cm
6.6m	6600g
0.6kg	660g
0.66kg	660cm
6.6kg	60cm

Alex is trying to teach Joe how different measures relate to each other. Can you help her by finishing her sentences?

(d) There are _____ m in 1km so there are _____ m in 3km.

(e) There are _____ mm in 1cm so there are _____ mm in 3cm.

(f) There are _____ ml in 1l so there are _____ ml in 3l.

(g) There are _____ cm in 1m so there are _____ cm in 3m.

(h) There are _____ g in 1kg so there are _____ g in 3kg.

Answers on page 128

PARENT TIP: Give children experience at measuring quantities in everyday life. For example, when cooking, decorating the house, planting in the garden, diluting drinks, and so on. Ask them what would be a suitable container or measuring tool for different situations.

123

Perimeter and area

Kirsty's family are redecorating their house. They need to measure each room for new skirting boards before the new carpets can go in. Can you help Kirsty and her family work out the perimeter and area for each room? Complete the table below.

	Length of room	Width of room	Skirting board perimeter	Carpet area
Dining room	6m	4m		
Kitchen	5m	3m		
Play room	3m	3m		
Bedroom 1	4m	4m		
Bedroom 2	4m	3m		

Kirsty and her family have forgotten to include the spare bedroom! They need 14m of skirting boards and 12m² for the carpet. What could the length and width of the room be?

....

....

Once the garage conversion is finished, they measure the perimeter for the skirting boards. Each wall is a whole number of metres. The total distance they measure is 18m. What could the walls measure? Can you find three different possible measurements? Write them below.

Answers on page 128

The utility room is a square shape with its area the same as its perimeter. What could the lengths of the walls be? Show your workings out.

....

....

The living room is a rectilinear shape.
What is the total length of skirting board and total area of carpet needed for the living room? Show your workings out.

....

....

....

3m

4m

7m

6m

3m

9m

Answers on page 128

PARENT TIP: Help your children to measure the length and width of the rooms in your house. Which room has the biggest floor area? Which room has the longest perimeter?

125

Telling the time

Dave works at the funfair. He does different jobs all through the day. Write the digital time he does each job in both 12 hour and 24 hour clock times.

a Running the rollercoaster

am

....

....

b Fixing the dodgems

am

....

....

c Selling candyfloss

pm

....

....

d Making balloon animals

pm

....

....

Dave is running late today and takes his break half an hour after he is supposed to. Show the time on each analogue clock half an hour after he was supposed to take his break.

Morning break

10:25am

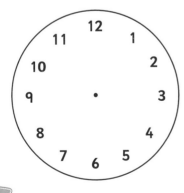

Lunch break

12:45am

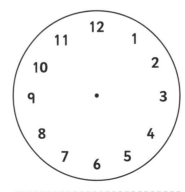

Afternoon break

2:20pm

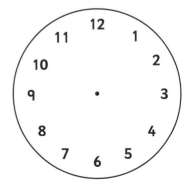

Answers on page 128

The clock in the staff room has lost its minute hand, but Dave says he can still use it to tell the time. Draw lines to match each clock face to the time it shows.

3:30pm

6:15pm

8:30am

2:45pm

Dave has to keep a log of when he closes the rides for cleaning. He writes the times down, but forgets to put them in the right order. Can you help him organise his log? Use the stickers to put the rides in the correct order from earliest to latest.

4:35 pm	Dodgems
11:42 am	Tea cups
3:12 pm	Carousel

09:30	Ferris wheel
15:47	Helter skelter
14:08	Pirate ship

1 ....

2 ....

3 ....

4 ....

5 ....

6 ....

Answers

Pages 98–99: Reading and comparing

Jenny: Three thousand and fifty; Mike: Two thousand, two hundred and forty-six; Alice: One thousand, three hundred and fifty-five.

Round 2 scores: Alice: £3355; Jenny: £2550; Mike: £2156, Steve: £2607. Round 3 scores: a. Alice must win £500. b. Jenny needs £600 to catch up with Steve. c. Mike needs to win £700 to pass his target. Alice: the computer added £500 to the total instead of subtracting £500. Jenny: the computer added £3000 instead of £300. Mike: The computer added £40 instead of £50. Steve: the computer subtracted £200 instead of adding £800.

Pages 100–101: Rounding

	Visitor numbers	Rounded to the nearest 10	Rounded to the nearest 100	Rounded to the nearest 1000
January	2345	2350	2300	2000
February	2767	2770	2800	3000
March	3698	3700	3700	4000
April	3064	3060	3100	3000
May	4002	4000	4000	4000
June	2986	2990	3000	3000

	Visitor numbers	Rounded to nearest 10	Rounded to nearest 100	Rounded to nearest 1000
July	2863	2860	2900	3000
August	2638	2640	2600	3000
September	3268	3270	3300	3000

a. the number of visitors could be any numbers between 2250 and 2349 inclusive. b. Highest: 2349, Lowest: 2250. c. Highest: 2449, Lowest: 2350. d. They both round to 4000. e. 3 ones round down to the nearest ten, but the nearest ten happens to be also a multiple of 100. f. 8499.

Pages 102–103: Adding 4-digit numbers

1. 5601, 2. 4023, 3. 4711, 4. 4800, 5. 5297.

Match 1 had the most supporters in total.

Sam was estimating Match 2 by adding 2200 + 1800.

Sam rounded to the nearest 100 while his dad rounded to the nearest 1000. Team A: 7295. Team B: 7287. Team A had the most supporters.

```
  2 7 6 5          3 2 1 4
+ 1 4 4 8        + 2 6 8 7
  4 2 1 3          5 9 0 1
```

1845 + 2000 − 1 = 384

Pages 104–105: Subtracting 4-digit numbers

a. £667, b. £1199, c. £180.

```
d.  3 0 5 8      e.  4 5 0 0      f.  2 4 5 0
  - 1 5 4 9        - 1 8 5 9        - 1 2 6 5
    1 5 0 9          2 6 4 1          1 1 8 5

    1 1 8 5          9 3 7          7 7 3          4 7 5
  -   2 4 8        - 1 6 4        - 2 9 8        - 3 2 9
      9 3 7          7 7 3          4 7 5          1 4 6
```

No.
Addition checks: Wildlife park: 9566, Water park: 7829. Mr Bailey made the mistake of always subtracting the smaller digit in each column from the larger digit.

Pages 106–107: Using times tables facts

Possible arrays are: 1 row of 18 stickers (1 x 18), 2 rows of 9 stickers (2 x 9), 3 rows of 6 stickers (3 x 6), 6 rows of 3 stickers (6 x 3), 9 rows of 2 stickers (9 x 2), 18 rows of 1 sticker (18 x 1).

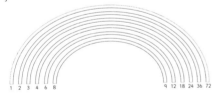

a. >, b. <, c. =, d. 420, e. 1500, f. 1600.

Pages 108–109: Multiplying and dividing mentally

Jack's number	Captain Multivide's power	New number
23	x 10	230
17	÷ 100	0.17
30	÷ 10	3
16	x 100	1600
12	÷ 10	1.2

a. x 10, b. x 100, c. ÷ 10

Jack's number	Captain Multivide's power	New number	What was his mistake?
34	x 100	340	He multiplied by 10 instead of 100.
23	÷ 10	230	He multiplied by 10 instead of dividing.
72	x 100	7200	He multiplied by 100 instead of 10.
20	÷ 100	2	He divided by 10 instead of 100.
9	÷ 10	0.09	He divided by 100 instead of 10.

d. 231, e. 0, f. 62, g. 560, h. 99, i. 0
Numbers multiplied by 1 stay the same size and don't get bigger. Numbers multiplied by 0 always become 0.

Pages 110–111: Multiplying 3-digit numbers

a. 1710, b. 402, c. 956, d. 1242, e. 1295. Jackie drove the most miles to the food factory. f. £1488, g. £952.

```
    2 3 5          1 7 8          1 8 6
  ×     8        ×     6        ×     5
  1 8 8 0        1 0 6 8          9 3 0
```

Pages 112–113: Equivalent fractions

a. $\frac{1}{3}$, b. $\frac{1}{4}$, c. $\frac{1}{6}$, d. $\frac{1}{6}$. e. Jeff has $\frac{1}{6}$ and Alan has $\frac{2}{12}$ which can be simplified to $\frac{1}{6}$. f. Both are right: $\frac{3}{12} = \frac{1}{4}$. g. Jeff has $\frac{2}{6}$ ($=\frac{1}{3}$), but Alan has $\frac{2}{12} = \frac{1}{6}$. h. $\frac{3}{8}$, i. $\frac{1}{4}$, j. $\frac{1}{8}$.

Other arrangements are possible.

Pages 114–115: Decimal numbers

a. 0.3m, b. 0.25m, c. 0.007m, d. $\frac{3}{10}$ = 0.3m, not 0.03m. $\frac{2}{100}$ = 0.02, $\frac{5}{100}$ = 0.05, $\frac{20}{100}$ = 0.2, $\frac{5}{10}$ = 0.5, $\frac{25}{100}$ = 0.25, $\frac{7}{100}$ = 0.07. $\frac{4}{10}$ < 0.5, $\frac{8}{100}$ = 0.08, 0.53 > 0.35, 0.17 < $\frac{2}{10}$, 0.06 < $\frac{6}{10}$, 0.5 > $\frac{35}{100}$.

Pages 116–117: Fraction problems

a. 4, b. 25, c. 24, d. 30. e. Yes. $\frac{1}{4}$ of 60 = 15 and $\frac{1}{2}$ of 60 = 30. 22 is between 15 and 30. f. 12. g. 45. h. Monday: 36, Tuesday: 40, Wednesday: 30 lengths. Sophie swam the most lengths on Tuesday. i. Monday: $\frac{1}{4}$. Tuesday: $\frac{1}{5}$, Wednesday: $\frac{1}{10}$, Thursday: $\frac{3}{10}$, Friday: $\frac{3}{20}$. j. Yes. 3 doesn't divide equally into 40. k. $\frac{1}{8}$, $\frac{2}{5}$, $\frac{3}{10}$ all make a complete number of lengths.

Pages 118–119: Shape properties

a.  b. c. d.

e. Isosceles, f. Right-angled, g. Equilateral, h. Scalene. i. Kite j. Trapezium. k. Always true: quad means 4. l. Never true: they can have one obtuse angle. m. Sometimes true: e.g. a square does, a rhombus doesn't.

Pages 120–121: Angles

Bike: Acute: b, c, d. Obtuse: a, e. House: Acute: c, d, e, f. Obtuse: a, b, g. Clocks: half past 3: 75°, 8 o' clock: 120°, 11 o' clock: 30°, half past 7: 45°.

a. True. b. True. c. False: 2 are acute and 2 are obtuse.

Pages 122–123: Units of measure

Freeze dried coffee: 3.5kg, Powdered milk: 12kg, Dehydrated vegetables: 55kg, Dried biscuits: 37.5kg, Heat treated tortillas: 20kg. a. 25 litres, b. 0.35km, c. 85cm.
0.06m – 6cm, 0.6m – 60cm, 6.6m – 660cm, 0.6kg – 600g, 0.66kg – 660g, 6.6kg – 6600g.
d. 1000, 3000, e. 10, 30, f. 1000, 3000, g. 100, 300, h. 1000, 3000.

Pages 124–125: Perimeter and area

Dining room: 20m, 24m²; Kitchen: 16m, 15m², Play room: 12m, 9m², Bedroom 2: 14m, 12m². Spare bedroom: 4m x 3m Possible pairs of measurements include: 5m x 4m, 6m x 3m, 7m x 2m, 8m x 1m. Utility room: 4m. Living room: 32m of skirting board, 39m² of carpet.

Pages 126–127: Telling the time

a. 8:30am, 08:30, b. 11:15am, 11:15, c. 1:30pm, 13:30, d. 3:40pm, 15.40.

2:45pm   8:30am   3:30pm   6:15pm

1.   2.   3.   4.   5.   6.